Fiona Mapp

Success

GCSE Mathematics
Higher
Revision Guide

Contents

4   Revision & exam tips

Number

Revised

5   Using a calculator
6   Types of numbers
8   Positive & negative numbers
10 Fractions
12 Decimals
14 Approximations & checking calculations
16 Percentages 1
18 Percentages 2
20 Fractions, decimals & percentages
21 Recurring decimals & surds
22 Ratio
24 Indices
26 Standard index form
28 Upper & lower bounds of measurement
30 Practice questions

Algebra

Revised

32 Algebra 1
34 Algebra 2
36 Equations 1
38 Equations 2
40 Number patterns & sequences
41 Inequalities
42 Formulae
44 The quadratic formula
45 Direct & inverse proportion
46 Straight-line graphs
48 Curved graphs
50 Advanced graphs
52 Interpreting graphs
54 Practice questions

Contents

2

Geometry and measures

Revised

56 Constructions & plans

58 Angles

60 Bearings & scale drawings

62 Transformations 1

64 Transformations 2

66 Similarity & congruency

68 Loci & coordinates in 3D

69 Angle properties of circles

70 Pythagoras' theorem

72 Trigonometry in right-angled triangles

74 Application of trigonometry

76 Further trigonometry

78 Measures & measurement

80 Area of 2D shapes

82 Volume of 3D shapes

84 Further length, area & volume

86 Vectors

88 Practice questions

Statistics and probability

Revised

90 Collecting data

92 Representing data

94 Scatter graphs & correlation

96 Averages 1

98 Averages 2

100 Cumulative frequency graphs

102 Histograms

104 Probability 1

106 Probability 2

108 Practice questions

110 Answers

IBC Index

Contents

3

Revision & exam tips

Exam preparation

The following tips will help to make your revision easier and the exams more stress free:

Make a revision plan. Draw up a plan covering all topics and set a realistic number of hours for revision each week. Note the dates of your exams and leave a week or two before each exam for final revision.

Start preparing for the exams early. Take breaks from revising, exercise regularly, and eat and sleep well.

Revise effectively. Short bursts of about 30 minutes followed by a break work best. Make your revision active – summarise your notes, highlight key points, draw diagrams, use post-it notes, ask someone to test you.

Boost your memory. Find ways of learning that suit you best. Try using images, mnemonics, rhymes and colour-coding to trigger your memory.

Practise questions. Highlight the key words in the question, plan your response and ensure that your answer is relevant. This Success Revision Guide features a spread of practice questions at the end of each section. For further revision, an accompanying Workbook is available packed full of practice questions.

Think positively. Look back at your original plan from time to time, and realise the progress you have made. If there are areas that you find particularly difficult, ask your teacher for help.

Allow time for final revision the week before the exam. Go over essential or difficult points.

The night before the exam, look over a few points but do not try to cram lots of new information. Get all your equipment ready – pens, pencils, calculator, etc. Have an early night.

Boosting your grade

The following tips will give you the best chance of success in your maths exams:

Follow all instructions in the exam paper. Some formulae are printed inside the exam paper. Remember they are there. You may need to use them.

Read each question carefully and ensure you answer the question. Check the number of marks available for each question and answer accordingly. Do not spend too much time on a question. You can come back to it later.

Show all your working. Marks may be gained for part answers, or for correct methods, even if the final answer is incorrect. If an incorrect answer is given without working, the mark will be zero.

Answers must be given to an **appropriate degree of accuracy**. Write down the calculator display in full. Leave rounding and correction until the final answer, unless directed otherwise. Always give units if they are not provided.

Graphs must be drawn with a sharp pencil, never pen. Remember to label the axes.

All your written work must be clear. The examiner is not used to your handwriting. Untidy, confused and messy answers can be misread and lose marks.

Keep an eye on the time – make sure you answer the correct number of questions and leave time to read through your answers.

Using a calculator

Order of operations

BIDMAS is a made-up word that helps you to remember the order in which calculations take place.

B I D M A S

↑ Brackets
↑ Indices
↑ Division
↑ Multiplication
↑ Addition
↑ Subtraction

BIDMAS simply means that anything in brackets is done first, then the other operations are done in the order shown.

For example:

$(2 + 4) \times 3 = 18$ but $2 + 4 \times 3 = 14$, **not** 18, because without the brackets the multiplication is done first.

Important calculator keys

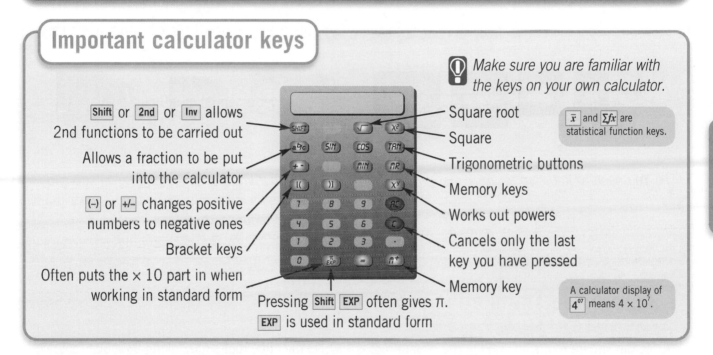

💡 *Make sure you are familiar with the keys on your own calculator.*

Shift or 2nd or Inv allows 2nd functions to be carried out

Allows a fraction to be put into the calculator

(−) or +/− changes positive numbers to negative ones

Bracket keys

Often puts the × 10 part in when working in standard form

Square root

Square

Trigonometric buttons

Memory keys

Works out powers

Cancels only the last key you have pressed

Memory key

$\bar{x}$ and Σfx are statistical function keys.

A calculator display of 4^{07} means 4×10^{7}.

Pressing Shift EXP often gives π.
EXP is used in standard form

Calculating powers

y^x or x^y is used for calculating powers such as 2^7.

Use the power key on your calculator to work out 2^7:
❶ Write down the calculator keys used.
❷ Check that you obtain the answer 128.

Now try writing down the keys that would be needed for the following calculations.

Check that you get the right answers.

$$\frac{2.9 \times 3.6}{(4.2 + 3.7)} = 1.322$$

$$9^{\frac{1}{3}} \times 4^5 = 2130$$

$$\frac{3 \times (5.2)^2}{9.6 \times (12.4)^3} = 4.432 \times 10^{-3}$$

Quick test

❶ Work out the following on your calculator. 🖩
a) $\dfrac{27.1 \times 6.4}{9.3 + 2.7}$
b) $\dfrac{(9.3)^4}{2.7 \times 3.6}$
c) $\sqrt{\dfrac{25^2}{4\pi}}$
d) $\frac{5}{9}(25 - 10)$

Types of numbers

Squares and cubes

Square numbers

Any number raised to the **power 2** gives a **square number**. For example, $6^2 = 6 \times 6 = 36$ (six squared).

Square numbers include:

1	4	9	16	25	36	49	64
(1 × 1)	(2 × 2)	(3 × 3)	(4 × 4)	(5 × 5)	(6 × 6)	(7 × 7)	(8 × 8)
81	100	121	144	169	196	225	
(9 × 9)	(10 × 10)	(11 × 11)	(12 × 12)	(13 × 13)	(14 × 14)	(15 × 15)	

Square numbers can be illustrated by drawing squares:

Cube numbers

Any number raised to the **power 3** gives a **cube number**. For example, $5^3 = 5 \times 5 \times 5 = 125$ (five cubed).

Cube numbers include:

1	8	27	64	125	1000
(1 × 1 × 1)	(2 × 2 × 2)	(3 × 3 × 3)	(4 × 4 × 4)	(5 × 5 × 5)	(10 × 10 × 10)

Cube numbers can be illustrated by drawing cubes:

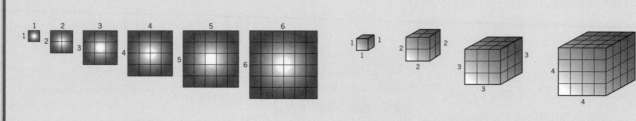

❗ *You need to know up to 15^2.*

❗ *It is important that you recognise square and cube numbers because they often appear in number sequence questions.*

Square roots and cube roots

$\sqrt{}$ is the square root sign. Taking the square root is the opposite of squaring.

For example, $\sqrt{25} = \pm 5$ since $5^2 = 25$, or $(-5)^2 = 25$

$\sqrt[3]{}$ is the cube root sign. Taking the cube root is the opposite of cubing.

For example, $\sqrt[3]{8} = 2$ since $2^3 = 8$

Multiples

Multiples are the numbers that appear in multiplication tables.

For example, multiples of 3 are 3, 6, 9, 12, 15, ...

Multiples of 8 are 8, 16, 24, 32, 40, ...

Reciprocals

The **reciprocal** of a number $\frac{a}{x}$ is $\frac{x}{a}$ $(= x \div a)$. Multiplying a number by its reciprocal always gives 1. Zero has no reciprocal, because division by zero is not defined.

For example:
- The reciprocal of $\frac{2}{3}$ is $\frac{3}{2}$
- The reciprocal of 4 is $\frac{1}{4}$ (4 is the same as $\frac{4}{1}$)
- To find the reciprocal of $1\frac{2}{3}$, first put it in the form $\frac{a}{x}$ ($1\frac{2}{3} = \frac{5}{3}$), then invert it to give $\frac{3}{5}$

Factors and prime numbers

Factors

Factors are whole numbers that divide exactly into another number. For example, the factors of 20 are 1, 2, 4, 5, 10, 20. To find all the factors of a number, start at 1 and divide by each whole number in turn. Factors can be split up into factor pairs. For example, for the factors of 20:

```
1  2  3  4  5  6  7  8  9  10 11 12 13 14 15 16 17 18 19 20
```

So, $1 \times 20 = 20$ $2 \times 10 = 20$ $4 \times 5 = 20$

Prime numbers

A **prime number** is a number that has only two factors, 1 and itself. Note that 1 is not a prime number. The prime numbers up to 20 are 2, 3, 5, 7, 11, 13, 17 and 19.

Prime factors

Prime factors are factors that are prime. All whole numbers can be written as products of their prime factors. For example, the diagram below shows the prime factors of 360:

1. Divide 360 by its first prime factor, 2.
2. Divide 180 by its first prime factor, 2. When 2 no longer works, try 3, then 5, and so on.
3. Keep on going until the final number is prime.
4. As a product of its prime factors, 360 can be written as:

   $2 \times 2 \times 2 \times 3 \times 3 \times 5 = 360$

   or in **index notation** (using powers):

   $2^3 \times 3^2 \times 5 = 360$

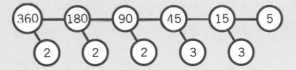

Highest common factor (HCF)

The **largest factor** that two numbers have in common is called the **HCF**.

Example

Find the HCF of 84 and 360.

1. Write the numbers as products of their prime factors and ring the common factors.

   $84 \ = (2) \times (2) \times \ (3) \ \ \ \ \ \ \times 7$
   $360 = (2) \times (2) \times 2 \times (3) \times 3 \times 5$

2. These give the HCF $= 2 \times 2 \times 3 = 12$

Lowest (least) common multiple (LCM)

The **LCM** is the lowest number that is a multiple of two or more numbers.

Example

Find the LCM of 6 and 8.

1. Write the numbers as products of their prime factors.

   $8 = 2 \times 2 \times (2)$
   $6 = \ \ \ \ \ \ \ \ (2) \times 3$

   8 and 6 have a common prime factor of 2. It is only counted once.

2. You take one number from each column, so the LCM of 6 and 8 is $2 \times 2 \times 2 \times 3 = 24$

Rational numbers

Rational numbers are numbers that **can** be expressed as a fraction, $\frac{a}{b}$, where a and b are integers.

Irrational numbers are numbers that **cannot** be written as a fraction,

e.g. $\sqrt{2}$, π, $(\sqrt{3} - 1)$, etc.

Quick test

1. List the prime numbers between 10 and 30.
2. Find the HCF and LCM of 24 and 60.
3. Find **a)** $\sqrt{64}$ **b)** $\sqrt[3]{216}$
4. Write down the reciprocals of the following:

   a) $\frac{9}{12}$ **b)** $\frac{x}{p}$ **c)** 5   **d)** $\frac{1}{10}$

Positive & negative numbers

Number

Directed numbers

Directed numbers are numbers that may be **positive** or **negative**. Positive numbers are above zero; negative numbers are below zero.

NEGATIVE   POSITIVE

-10 -9 -8 -7 -6 -5 -4 -3 -2 -1 0 1 2 3 4 5 6 7 8 9 10

GETTING SMALLER   GETTING BIGGER

For example:
-10 is smaller than -8 or -10 < -8
-4 is bigger than -8   or   -4 > -8
2 is bigger than -6   or   2 > -6

Directed numbers are often seen on the weather forecast in winter. Quite often the temperature is below 0°C.

Aberdeen is the coldest place on this forecast map at -8°C. London is 6 degrees warmer than Manchester.

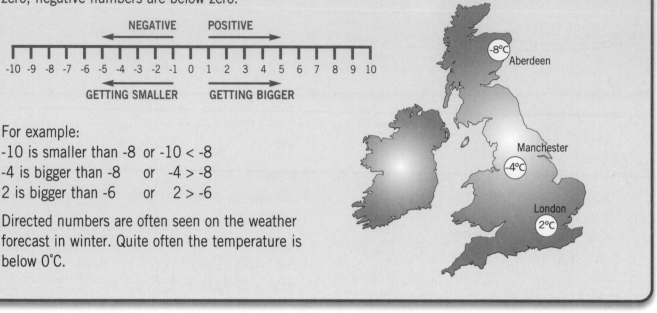

-8°C Aberdeen

Manchester -4°C

London 2°C

Integers

Integers are whole numbers that can be positive or negative. Here is a set of integers:
{..., -3, -2, -1, 0, 1, 2, 3, ...}.

When referring to integers, the term **integral value** is used.

A number that is **non-integral** is not an integer.

For example, the winning numbers on the lottery are:
16 34 49 7 1 19

When put in order they would look like:
1 7 16 19 34 49

Multiplying and dividing directed numbers

Multiply and divide directed numbers as normal. Then find the sign for the answer using these rules:
- Two **like** signs (both + or both -) give a positive answer.
- Two **unlike** signs (one + and the other -) give a negative answer.

For example:
$-6 \times (+4) = -24$ $-12 \div (-3) = 4$
$-6 \times (-3) = 18$ $20 \div (-4) = -5$

$(+) \times (+) = +$
$(-) \times (-) = +$
$(+) \times (-) = -$
$(-) \times (+) = -$

$(+) \div (+) = +$
$(-) \div (-) = +$
$(+) \div (-) = -$
$(-) \div (+) = -$

You need to remember the rules of multiplication and division. You will find these laws useful when multiplying out brackets in algebra.

Adding and subtracting directed numbers

Number lines can help you to understand the concept of adding and subtracting directed numbers.

The temperature at 6am was -5°C. By 10am it had risen 8 degrees.

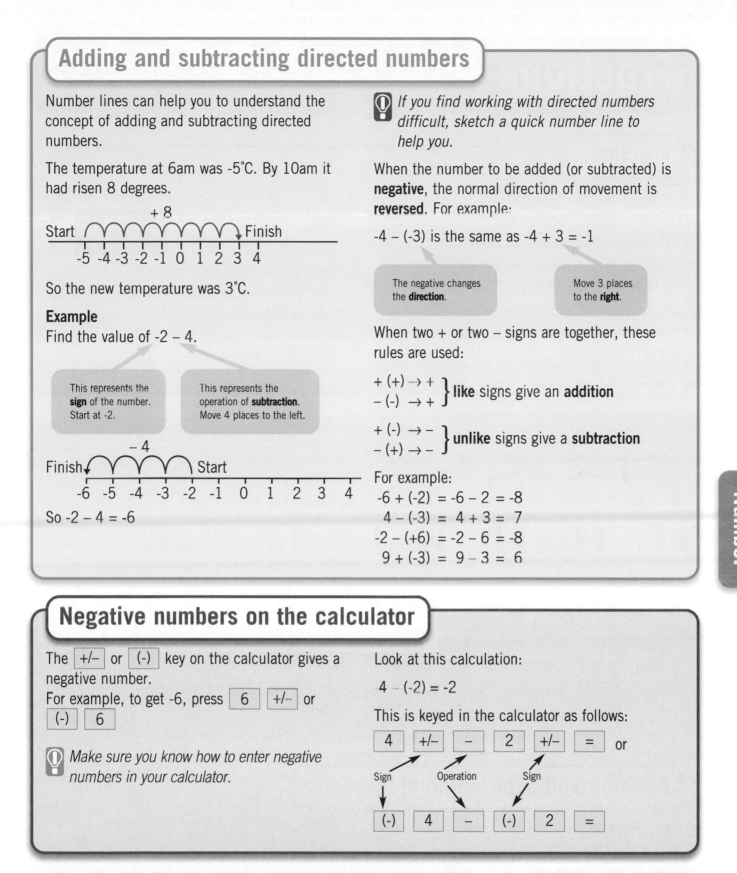

So the new temperature was 3°C.

Example
Find the value of -2 – 4.

This represents the **sign** of the number. Start at -2.

This represents the operation of **subtraction**. Move 4 places to the left.

So -2 – 4 = -6

If you find working with directed numbers difficult, sketch a quick number line to help you.

When the number to be added (or subtracted) is **negative**, the normal direction of movement is **reversed**. For example:

-4 – (-3) is the same as -4 + 3 = -1

The negative changes the **direction**.

Move 3 places to the **right**.

When two + or two – signs are together, these rules are used:

$$+ (+) \rightarrow +$$
$$- (-) \rightarrow +$$
like signs give an **addition**

$$+ (-) \rightarrow -$$
$$- (+) \rightarrow -$$
unlike signs give a **subtraction**

For example:
$$-6 + (-2) = -6 - 2 = -8$$
$$4 - (-3) = 4 + 3 = 7$$
$$-2 - (+6) = -2 - 6 = -8$$
$$9 + (-3) = 9 - 3 = 6$$

Negative numbers on the calculator

The $\boxed{+/-}$ or $\boxed{(-)}$ key on the calculator gives a negative number.
For example, to get -6, press $\boxed{6}$ $\boxed{+/-}$ or $\boxed{(-)}$ $\boxed{6}$

Make sure you know how to enter negative numbers in your calculator.

Look at this calculation:

$$4 - (-2) = -2$$

This is keyed in the calculator as follows:

$\boxed{4}$ $\boxed{+/-}$ $\boxed{-}$ $\boxed{2}$ $\boxed{+/-}$ $\boxed{=}$ or

Sign   Operation   Sign

$\boxed{(-)}$ $\boxed{4}$ $\boxed{-}$ $\boxed{(-)}$ $\boxed{2}$ $\boxed{=}$

Quick test

❶ If the temperature was -12°C at 2am, and it increased by 15 degrees by 11am, what was the temperature at 11am?

❷ Without using a calculator, work out the following:
   a) -2 – (-6)
   b) -9 + (-7)
   c) -2 × 6
   d) -9 + (-3)
   e) -20 ÷ (-4)
   f) -18 ÷ (-3)
   g) 4 – (-3)
   h) -7 + (-3)
   i) -9 × -4

Fractions

Fractions

A fraction is a part of a whole.
The top number is the **numerator**.
The bottom number is the **denominator**.

A fraction like $\frac{4}{5}$ is called a **proper fraction** because the **denominator is greater** than the numerator.

A fraction like $\frac{24}{17}$ is called an **improper fraction** because the **numerator is greater** than the denominator.

A fraction like $2\frac{1}{2}$ is called a **mixed number**.

$\frac{4}{5}$ means 4 parts out of 5.

When expressing one amount as a fraction of another amount, write them as a fraction with the first amount the numerator and the second amount the denominator. For example, 7 as a fraction of 9 is written as $\frac{7}{9}$

Equivalent fractions

Equivalent fractions have the same value.
For example:

From the diagrams it can be seen that

$$\frac{1}{2} = \frac{2}{4} = \frac{3}{6} = \frac{4}{8}$$

They are equivalent fractions. Fractions can be changed to their equivalents by **multiplying** or **dividing** both the numerator and denominator by the same amount.

Examples

a) Change $\frac{5}{7}$ to its equivalent fraction with a denominator of 28.

Multiply the top and bottom by 4.
So $\frac{5}{7}$ is equivalent to $\frac{20}{28}$

b) Change $\frac{40}{60}$ to its equivalent fraction with a denominator of 3.

Divide the top and bottom by 20.
So $\frac{40}{60}$ is equivalent to $\frac{2}{3}$

This is known as simplifying the fraction by '**cancelling**'.

Addition and subtraction of fractions

These examples show the basic principles of adding and subtracting fractions.

Examples

a) Work out $\frac{1}{8} + \frac{3}{4}$

❶ First make the denominators the same: $\frac{3}{4}$ is **equivalent** to $\frac{6}{8}$

❷ Replace $\frac{3}{4}$ with $\frac{6}{8}$ to make $\frac{1}{8} + \frac{6}{8}$

❸ Add the numerators $1 + 6 = 7$.
The denominator stays the same.
So, $\frac{1}{8} + \frac{6}{8} = \frac{7}{8}$

b) Work out $\frac{9}{12} - \frac{1}{3}$

❶ First make the denominators the same: $\frac{1}{3}$ is equivalent to $\frac{4}{12}$

❷ Replace the $\frac{1}{3}$ with $\frac{4}{12}$

❸ Subtract the numerators but **not** the denominators. The denominator stays the same.

So, $\frac{9}{12} - \frac{4}{12} = \frac{5}{12}$

Or, $\frac{9-4}{12} = \frac{5}{12}$

Number

Multiplication and division of fractions

When multiplying and dividing fractions, write out whole or mixed numbers as improper fractions before starting. For example:

$$1\frac{2}{9} \times \frac{4}{7} = \frac{11}{9} \times \frac{4}{7} = \frac{44}{63}$$

> Multiply numerators together.
> Multiply denominators together.

Change a division into a multiplication by turning the second fraction upside down and multiplying both fractions together; in other words, to divide by a fraction, **multiply by the reciprocal**.

Example

Work out $\frac{7}{9} \div \frac{12}{18}$

1. Take the **reciprocal** of the **second fraction**.
2. Multiply the fractions as normal.
   So, $\frac{7}{9} \times \frac{18}{12} = \frac{126}{108}$
3. Rewrite the answer as a mixed number.
   $\frac{126}{108} = 1\frac{18}{108} = 1\frac{1}{6}$

Using the fraction key on the calculator

$a^{b/c}$ is the fraction key on the calculator.
For example, 12 out of 18 can be written as $\frac{12}{18}$
$\frac{12}{18}$ is keyed in as $\boxed{1}\ \boxed{2}\ \boxed{a^{b/c}}\ \boxed{1}\ \boxed{8}$

This is displayed as $\boxed{12\lrcorner18}$ or $\boxed{12\text{-}18}$

The calculator will automatically cancel down fractions when the $\boxed{=}$ key is pressed.

For example, $\frac{12}{18}$ becomes $\boxed{2\lrcorner3}$ or $\boxed{2\text{-}3}$
This means two-thirds.

A display of $\boxed{1\lrcorner4\lrcorner9}$ means $1\frac{4}{9}$. If you now press $\boxed{shift}\ \boxed{a^{b/c}}$, it converts back to an improper fraction, $\boxed{13\lrcorner9}$, which means $\frac{13}{9}$

💡 *Check how to use your calculator.*

Proportional changes with fractions

Increase and decrease
There are two methods for working out proportional changes with fractions. Use the one that is familiar to you. Remember that 'of' means multiply.

Example
Last year a gym had 290 members. This year there are $\frac{3}{5}$ more. How many members are there now?

Method 1
1. Work out $\frac{3}{5}$ **of** 290. $\frac{1}{5} = 58$, so $\frac{3}{5} \times 290 = 174$
2. Add this to the original number, so
   $290 + 174 = 464$ people.

Method 2
Increasing by $\frac{3}{5}$ is the same as multiplying by $1\frac{3}{5}$ $(1 + \frac{3}{5})$.
On the calculator, key in

$\boxed{1}\ \boxed{a^{b/c}}\ \boxed{3}\ \boxed{a^{b/c}}\ \boxed{5}\ \boxed{\times}\ \boxed{290}\ \boxed{=}$

$1\frac{3}{5} \times 290 = 464$

💡 *Make sure you know how to use your calculator to add, subtract, multiply and divide fractions.*

Quick test

1. Without using a calculator, work out the following:
   a) $\frac{2}{9} + \frac{3}{27}$ b) $\frac{3}{5} - \frac{1}{4}$ c) $\frac{6}{9} \times \frac{72}{104}$ d) $\frac{8}{9} \div \frac{2}{3}$
   e) $\frac{4}{7} - \frac{1}{3}$ f) $\frac{2}{7} \div 1\frac{1}{2}$ g) $\frac{7}{11} \div \frac{22}{14}$ h) $\frac{2}{9} + \frac{4}{7}$

2. Calculate $\frac{2}{9}$ of £180. 🖩

3. $\frac{7}{12}$ more rain fell this year than last year. If 156mm fell last year, how much rain fell this year? 🖩

Decimals

Types of decimals

A **decimal point** is used to separate whole number columns from fractional columns.

For example:

Decimal point

Thousands	Hundreds	Tens	Units		Tenths	Hundredths	Thousandths
8	9	2	4	•	1	6	3

The 1 means $\frac{1}{10}$, the 6 means $\frac{6}{100}$, the 3 means $\frac{3}{1000}$

Terminating and recurring decimals

A decimal that stops is called a terminating decimal. All terminating decimals can be written as a fraction. For example:

$$0.273 = \frac{273}{1000} \quad 0.49 = \frac{49}{100} \quad 0.7 = \frac{7}{10}$$

If a fraction written in its simplest form has a denominator with a prime factor other than 2 or 5, it will convert to a recurring decimal.

A decimal that recurs is shown by placing a dot over the numbers that repeat. For example:

$$0.333... = 0.\dot{3}$$
$$0.177\,77... = 0.1\dot{7}$$
$$0.232\,323... = 0.\dot{2}\dot{3}$$
$$0.142\,857\,142\,857... = 0.\dot{1}42\,85\dot{7}$$

Decimal places (d.p.)

When rounding numbers to a specified number of **decimal places**, follow these steps:

1. Look at the last number that is wanted (e.g. if rounding 12.367 to 2 d.p. look at the 6 which is in the second d.p.).
2. Look at the number to the right of it (the number that is not needed – i.e. the 7).
3. If it is **5 or more**, then **round up the last digit** that is wanted (7 is greater than 5, so round up the 6 to a 7, i.e. 12.37).
4. If it is **less than 5**, then the digit remains the **same**.

For example:
12.49 = 12.5 to 1 d.p.
8.735 = 8.74 to 2 d.p.
9.624 = 9.62 to 2 d.p.

In athletics, times are usually rounded to 2 decimal places. The men's 100m world record holder in 2009 was Usain Bolt, of Jamaica, with a time of 9.58 seconds (2 d.p.).

Ordering decimals

When ordering decimals, follow these steps:
1. First write them all with the same number of digits after the decimal point.
2. Then compare whole numbers, digits in the tenths place, digits in the hundredths place, and so on.

Example

Arrange these numbers in order of size, smallest first:
6.21, 6.023, 6.4, 6.04, 2.71, 9.4

1. First rewrite them:
   6.210, 6.023, 6.400, 6.040, 2.710, 9.400
2. Then re-order them:
   2.710, 6.023, 6.040, 6.210, 6.400, 9.400
3. Rewrite in original form:
   2.71, 6.023, 6.04, 6.21, 6.4, 9.4

Remember, hundredths are smaller than tenths: $\frac{10}{100} = \frac{1}{10}$ *so* $\frac{6}{100} < \frac{1}{10}$

Multiplying and dividing by numbers between 0 and 1

When **multiplying** by numbers between 0 and 1, the result is **smaller** than the starting value.

When **dividing** by numbers between 0 and 1, the result is **bigger** than the starting value.

For example:

$6 \times 0.1 = 0.6$ $6 \div 0.1 = 60$
$6 \times 0.01 = 0.06$ $6 \div 0.01 = 600$
$6 \times 0.001 = 0.006$ $6 \div 0.001 = 6000$

The results are all smaller than the starting values.

The results are all bigger than the starting values.

Calculations with decimals

When **adding** and **subtracting** decimals, the decimal points need to go under each other. For example:

27.46
7.291 +
34.751

$17.\overset{6}{\cancel{0}}\overset{9}{\cancel{0}}\overset{1}{\cancel{0}}$
12.84
4.16

Line up the digits carefully. Put the decimal points under each other. The decimal point in the answer will be in line.

When **dividing** decimals, divide as normal, placing the decimal points in line. For example:

4.8
3)14.²4

Put the decimal points in line.

A fraction can be changed into a decimal by dividing the numerator by the denominator. For example, this is how you would change $\frac{3}{5}$ into a decimal by short division.

0.6
5)3.³0

When **dividing** by a decimal, it is easier to multiply the numerator and denominator by a power of 10, so that it becomes equivalent to a division with a whole number. For example:

$\frac{2.75}{0.25} = \frac{275}{25}$

Multiply the numerator and denominator by 100.

$= 11$

When **multiplying** decimals, the answer must have the same number of decimal places as the total number of decimal places in the numbers that are being multiplied.

Examples

a) Work out 24.6×7

246
7 ×
1722
³ ⁴

Multiply 246 by 7 = 1722, ignoring the decimal point. 24.6 has 1 number after the decimal point. The answer must have 1 decimal place (1 d.p.).

So $24.6 \times 7 = 172.2$

b) Work out 4.52×0.2

452
2 ×
904
¹

Work out 452×2, ignoring the decimal points. 4.52 has 2 d.p.; 0.2 has 1 d.p. So the answer must have 3 d.p.

$904 \longrightarrow 0.904$ Move the digits 3 places to the right.

So $4.52 \times 0.2 = 0.904$

c) Given that $4.28 \times 3.6 = 15.408$, find the value of...

Multiply 4.28 by 100 to give 428, so multiply 15.408 by 100.

i) 428×3.6
$4.28 \times 3.6 = 15.408$
So, $428 \times 3.6 = 1540.8$

ii) $154.08 \div 36$
$154.08 \div 36 = 4.28$

Since the numerator and denominator have both been multiplied by 10, the answer remains the same.

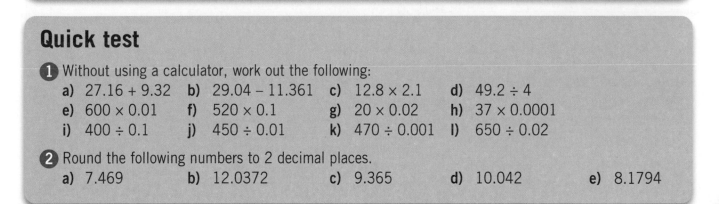

Quick test

1 Without using a calculator, work out the following:
a) $27.16 + 9.32$ b) $29.04 - 11.361$ c) 12.8×2.1 d) $49.2 \div 4$
e) 600×0.01 f) 520×0.1 g) 20×0.02 h) 37×0.0001
i) $400 \div 0.1$ j) $450 \div 0.01$ k) $470 \div 0.001$ l) $650 \div 0.02$

2 Round the following numbers to 2 decimal places.
a) 7.469 b) 12.0372 c) 9.365 d) 10.042 e) 8.1794

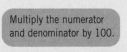

Number

Approximations & checking calculations

Significant figures (s.f. or sig. fig.)

The first significant figure is the first digit that is not zero. The 2nd, 3rd, 4th, ... significant figures follow on after the first digit. They may or may not be zeros. For example:

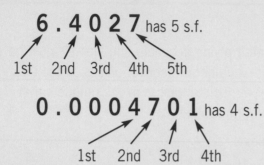

Take care when rounding that you do not change the place values.

To round a number to a given number of significant places, apply the same rule as with decimal places: if the next digit is 5 or more, round up. For example:

Number	to 3 s.f.	to 2 s.f.	to 1 s.f.
4.207	4.21	4.2	4
4379	4380	4400	4000
0.006 209	0.006 21	0.0062	0.006

After rounding the last digit, you must fill in the end zeros. For example, 4380 = 4400 to 2 s.f. (not 44).

In 2009, the tallest structure in the world was the Burj Khalifa at a height of 828m; that is 800m correct to 1 s.f.

Estimates and approximations

Estimating is a good way of checking answers. Follow these steps when estimating:

1. Round the numbers to 'easy' numbers, usually ones with 1 or 2 significant figures.
2. Work out the estimate using these easy numbers.
3. Use the symbol ≈, which means '**approximately equal to**'.
4. For multiplying or dividing, never approximate a number to zero. Use 0.1, 0.01, 0.001, etc.

For example:
$8.93 \times 25.09 \approx 10 \times 25 = 250$

$(6.29)^2 \approx 6^2 = 36$

$\dfrac{296 \times 52.1}{9.72 \times 1.14} \approx \dfrac{300 \times 50}{10 \times 1} = \dfrac{15\,000}{10} = 1500$

$0.096 \times 79.2 \approx 0.1 \times 80 = 8$

Questions that involve approximating are common on the non-calculator paper. For most of these questions, you are expected to round to 1 significant figure. Even if you find the calculation difficult, show your approximations to pick up method marks.

Example
Jack does the calculation $\dfrac{9.6 \times 103}{(2.9)^2}$

a) Estimate the answer to this calculation, without using a calculator.

$\dfrac{9.6 \times 103}{(2.9)^2} \approx \dfrac{10 \times 100}{3^2} = \dfrac{1000}{9} \approx \dfrac{1000}{10} = 100$

b) Jack's answer is 1175.7. Is this the right order of magnitude (about the right size)?

Jack's answer is not the right order of magnitude. It is 10 times too big.

When adding and subtracting, very small numbers may be approximated to zero.

For example:
$109.6 + 0.0002 \approx 110 + 0 = 110$

$63.87 - 0.01 \approx 64 - 0 = 64$

Checking calculations

When checking calculations, the process used can be reversed. For example:

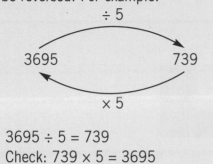

$$3695 \div 5 = 739$$
Check: $739 \times 5 = 3695$

$$106 \times 3 = 318$$
Check: $318 \div 3 = 106$

Calculations

When solving problems the answers should be rounded sensibly.

For example:
$$95.26 \times 6.39 = 608.7114 = 608.71 \text{ (2 d.p.)}$$

Round to 2 d.p. because the values in the question are to 2 d.p.

Examples

a) Jackie has £9.37. She divides it as equally as she can between 5 people. How much does each person receive?

$$£9.37 \div 5 = £1.874$$
$$= £1.87$$
(Round to 2 d.p. as it is money.)

(!) *You will lose marks if you do not write money to 2 d.p. If the answer to a money calculation is £9.7, always write it to 2 d.p., i.e. £9.70*

b) Paint is sold in 8-litre tins. Sandra needs 27 litres of paint. How many tins must she buy?

$$27 \div 8 = 3 \text{ remainder } 3$$

Sandra needs 4 tins of paint. Sandra would not have enough paint with 3 tins – she would be 3 litres short. Hence, the number of tins of paint must be rounded up.

(!) *When rounding remainders, consider the context of the question.*

Quick test

❶ Round the following numbers to 3 significant figures.
   a) 0.003 786 b) 27 490   c) 307 250

❷ Estimate the answer to $\dfrac{(29.4)^2 + 106}{2.2 \times 5.1}$

❸ Sukhvinder decided to decorate her living room. The total area of the walls was 48m². If one roll of wallpaper covers 5m² of wall, how many rolls of wallpaper did Sukhvinder need?

❹ Thomas earned £171.35 for working a 23-hour week. How much was he paid per hour? Check your calculation by estimating. 🖩

❺ The length of the River Nile is 6650km. What is the length of the River Nile correct to 2 significant figures?

Percentages 1

Percentages

Percentages are fractions with a denominator of 100.

% is the percentage sign.

75% means $\frac{75}{100}$ (this is also equal to $\frac{3}{4}$).

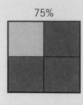
75%

Percentage of a quantity

The word '**of**' means **multiply**. For example,
40% of £600 becomes $\frac{40}{100} \times 600 = £240$

On the calculator, key in

40	÷	100	×	600	=

To work this out without a calculator, follow these steps:

❶ Work out 10% first by dividing by 10.
600 ÷ 10 = £60

❷ Multiply by 4 to get 40%.
4 × 60 = £240

 Percentage questions appear frequently at GCSE. They also often appear in everyday situations.

Example
A meal for four costs £92.20. VAT (value added tax) is charged at 17.5%.

a) How much VAT is there to pay on the meal?

$$17.5\% \text{ of } £92.20 = \frac{17.5}{100} \times 92.20$$
$$= £16.14 \text{ (to the nearest penny)}$$
$$\text{VAT} = £16.14$$

b) What is the final price of the meal?

Price of meal = £92.20 + £16.14 = £108.34

An alternative is to use the **multiplier method**:
An increase of 17.5% is the same as multiplying by 1.175, i.e. $1 + \frac{17.5}{100}$
£92.20 × 1.175
= £108.34 (to the nearest penny)

Percentage increase and decrease

The answers to these questions will be a percentage, so multiply the change by 100%.

$$\text{Percentage change} = \frac{\text{change}}{\text{original}} \times 100\%$$

Examples
a) A coat costs £125. In a sale it is reduced to £85. What is the percentage reduction?

Reduction = £125 – £85 = £40
$$\% \text{ reduction} = \frac{40}{125} \times 100\%$$
$$= 32\%$$

b) Matthew bought a flat for £145000. Three years later, he sold it for £162000. What was his percentage profit?

Profit = £162000 – £145000
= £17000
$$\% \text{ profit} = \frac{17000}{145000} \times 100\%$$
$$= 11.72\%$$

One quantity as a percentage of another

Again, to make the answer a percentage, multiply by 100%.

$$\text{Fraction} \xrightarrow{\times 100\%} \text{Percentage}$$

Example

In a carton of milk, 6.2g of the contents are fat. If 2.5g of the fat is saturated, what percentage of the total fat content is this?

$$\frac{2.5}{6.2} \times 100\% = 40.3\% \text{ (1 d.p.)}$$

On the calculator, key in

$$\boxed{2.5} \quad \boxed{\div} \quad \boxed{6.2} \quad \boxed{\times} \quad \boxed{100} \quad \boxed{=}$$

Reverse percentage problems

In reverse percentage problems, the **original quantity** is calculated.

Example

The price of a television is reduced by 20% in the sales. It now costs £250. What was the original price?

❶ The sale price is 100% – 20% = 80% of the pre-sale price.

$$\frac{80}{100} = 0.8 \text{ (this is the multiplier)}$$

0.8 × (original price) = £250

So, original price $= \frac{250}{0.8} = £312.50$

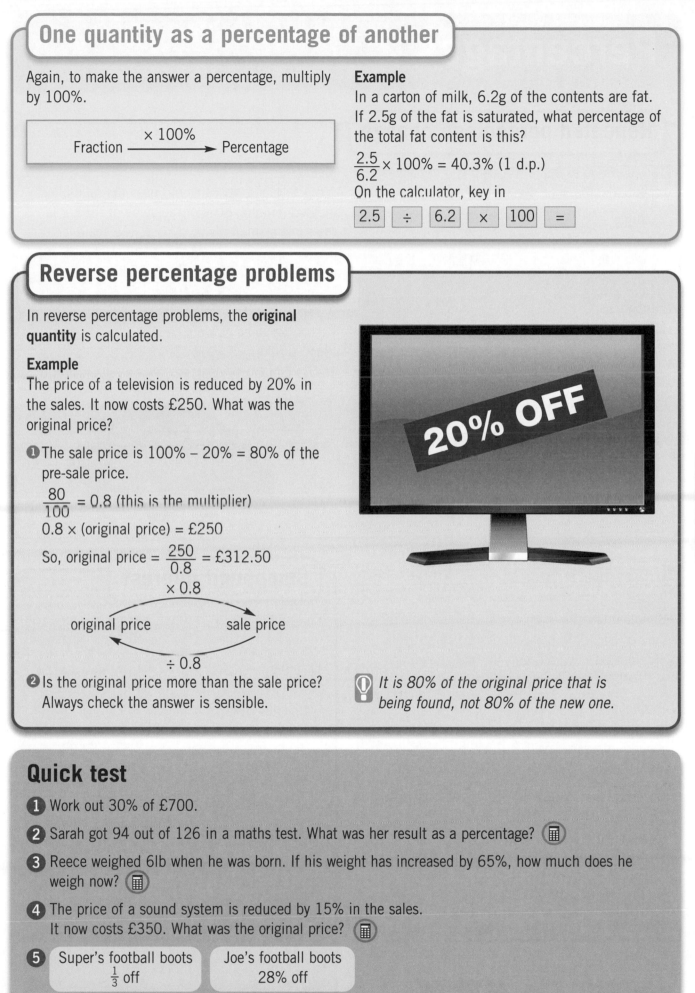

original price ⟷ sale price

× 0.8 (top arrow)

÷ 0.8 (bottom arrow)

❷ Is the original price more than the sale price? Always check the answer is sensible.

It is 80% of the original price that is being found, not 80% of the new one.

Number

Quick test

❶ Work out 30% of £700.

❷ Sarah got 94 out of 126 in a maths test. What was her result as a percentage?

❸ Reece weighed 6lb when he was born. If his weight has increased by 65%, how much does he weigh now?

❹ The price of a sound system is reduced by 15% in the sales. It now costs £350. What was the original price?

❺
Super's football boots	Joe's football boots
$\frac{1}{3}$ off	28% off

If a pair of football boots costs £49.99, which shop is selling them cheaper in the sale and what is their price?

Percentages 2

Repeated percentage change

The following example will help you to calculate repeated percentage change.

Example
A car was bought for £8000 in 2007. Each year it depreciated in value by 20%. What was the car worth 3 years later?

Method 1
❶ First find 80% of the original value of the car.

Year 1 $\dfrac{80}{100} \times £8000 = £6400$

❷ Then work out the value year by year.

Year 2 $\dfrac{80}{100} \times £6400 = £5120$

(£6400 depreciated in value by 20%)

Year 3 $\dfrac{80}{100} \times £5120 = £4096$ after 3 years

(£5120 depreciated in value by 20%)

🔔 Beware! Do not do 3 × 20 = 60% reduction over 3 years!

Method 2
A quick way to work this out uses the **multiplier method**. Finding 80% of the value of the car is the same as multiplying by 0.8. The scale factor is 0.8.

Year 1   0.8 × £8000 = £6400
Year 2   0.8 × £6400 = £5120
Year 3   0.8 × £5120 = £4096

This is the same as working out

$(0.8)^3 \times 8000 = £4096$

This is a much quicker way, if you understand it!

Simple interest

Simple interest is the interest that is sometimes paid on money in banks and building societies. The interest is paid each year (**per annum** or **p.a.**) and is the same amount each year.

Example
Jonathan has £2500 in his savings account. Simple interest is paid at 4.4% p.a. How much does he have in his account at the end of the year?

Increasing by 4.4% is the same as multiplying by 100 + 4.4 = 104.4%.

Total savings = $£2500 \times \dfrac{104.4}{100} = £2610$

(Interest paid = £2610 – £2500 = £110)

Note: If the money was in the account for 4 years, simple interest at the end of the 4 years would be 4 × £110 = £440.

Compound interest

Compound interest is where banks pay interest on the interest earned as well as on the original sum.

Example
Jonathan has £2500 in his savings account. Compound interest is paid at 4.4% p.a. How much will he have in his account after 4 years?

Method 1
Year 1: $\dfrac{104.4}{100} \times £2500 = £2610$
Year 2: 1.044 × £2610 = £2724.84
Year 3: 1.044 × £2724.84 = £2844.73
Year 4: 1.044 × £2844.73 = £2969.90
Total = £2969.90 (to the nearest penny)

Method 2
Using the multiplier method:

$\dfrac{104.4}{100} = 1.044$ is the scale factor

$= 2500 \times (1.044)^4$

Total = £2969.90 (to the nearest penny)

On a calculator, key in

| 2500 | × | 1.044 | x^y | 4 | = |

Number

National Insurance and tax

National Insurance

National Insurance (NI) is usually deducted from a wage as a percentage.

Example

Sue earns £1402.65 a month. National Insurance is deducted at 11%. How much NI must she pay?

$$11\% \text{ of } £1402.65 = 0.11 \times £1402.65$$
$$= £154.29$$

Income tax

A percentage of a wage or salary is deducted as **income tax**. **Personal allowances** must first be deducted in order to obtain the **taxable income**.

Examples

a) Harold earns £190 per week. The first £62 is not taxable; the remainder is taxed at 20%. How much income tax does he pay each week?

$$\text{Taxable income} = £190 - £62 = £128$$
$$20\% \text{ tax} = 0.2 \times £128 = £25.60$$
$$\text{Tax per week} = £25.60$$

b) Emily earns £48 500 per year. Her personal allowance is £6475. Her income is then taxed at 20% up to £37 400 and then at 40% above £37 400. How much does Emily earn after tax?

$$\text{Taxable income} = £48 500 - £6475 = £42 025$$
$$20\% \text{ tax} = 0.2 \times £37 400 = £7480$$
$$40\% \text{ tax on } (£42 025 - £37 400) = £4625$$
$$0.4 \times 4625 = £1850$$
$$\text{Total tax} = £7480 + £1850 = £9330$$
$$\text{Earnings} = £48 500 - £9330 = £39 170$$

Being able to answer questions like the examples in this section is important – not only because they often appear on the GCSE examination paper but because they also appear in everyday situations.

There are really only two types of percentage questions:

- *'Percentage of' – here you are given the percentage, so you divide by 100.*
- *Finding a percentage – here you need to work out a percentage so you multiply a fraction or a decimal by 100.*

Quick test

1. Charlotte has £4250 in the bank. If the interest rate is 3.8% p.a., how much interest on the savings will she get at the end of the year?

2. A car costs £6000 cash, or can be bought by hire purchase with a 30% deposit followed by 12 monthly instalments of £365. Find...
   a) the deposit
   b) the total amount paid for the car on hire purchase.

3. A house was bought in 2007 for £175 000. The price increased by 20% in 2008 and then decreased in value by 5% in 2009. How much was the house worth at the end of 2009?

4. Fiona has £3200 in savings. If compound interest is paid at 3% p.a., how much will she have in her account after three years?

Fractions, decimals & percentages

Number

Ordering fractions

When ordering fractions it is useful to write them with a **common denominator** so that you can compare the numerators.

Example

Place these fractions in order of size, smallest first:
$\frac{1}{4}, \frac{3}{10}, \frac{5}{8}, \frac{7}{20}, \frac{27}{40}$

Since all the fractions can be written with a denominator of 40, we can compare the numerators.
$\frac{10}{40}, \frac{12}{40}, \frac{25}{40}, \frac{14}{40}, \frac{27}{40}$

In size order:
$\frac{10}{40}, \frac{12}{40}, \frac{14}{40}, \frac{25}{40}, \frac{27}{40} = \frac{1}{4}, \frac{3}{10}, \frac{7}{20}, \frac{5}{8}, \frac{27}{40}$

Fractions to decimals to percentages

Equivalent fractions, decimals and percentages are all different ways of expressing the same number.

The table opposite shows...
- some common fractions and their **equivalents**, which you need to learn
- how to convert fractions to decimals to percentages.

> Get a friend to test you on the equivalences between fractions, decimals and percentages. You need to learn all the ones in the table.

Fraction	Decimal	Percentage
$\frac{1}{2}$	0.5	50%
$\frac{1}{3}$	$0.\dot{3}$	$33.\dot{3}\%$
$\frac{2}{3}$	$0.\dot{6}$	$66.\dot{6}\%$
$\frac{1}{4}$	0.25	25%
$\frac{3}{4}$	$\xrightarrow{3 \div 4}$ 0.75 $\xrightarrow{\times 100\%}$	75%
$\frac{1}{5}$	0.2	20%
$\frac{1}{8}$	0.125	12.5%
$\frac{3}{8}$	0.375	37.5%
$\frac{1}{10}$	0.1	10%
$\frac{1}{100}$	0.01	1%

Ordering different types of numbers

When putting a mixture of fractions, decimals and percentages in order of size, it is best to change them all to decimals first.

Example

Place the following in order of size, smallest first:
$\frac{3}{5}$, 0.65, 0.273, 27%, 62%, $\frac{4}{9}$

0.6, 0.65, 0.273, 0.27, 0.62, $0.\dot{4}$ — Put into decimals first.

0.27, 0.273, $0.\dot{4}$, 0.6, 0.62, 0.65 — Place in order of size, smallest first.

27%, 0.273, $\frac{4}{9}$, $\frac{3}{5}$, 62%, 0.65 — Rewrite.

Quick test

1 Change the following fractions into **a)** decimals **b)** percentages.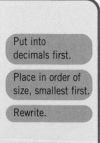

i) $\frac{2}{7}$ ii) $\frac{3}{5}$ iii) $\frac{8}{9}$

2 Place these numbers in order of size, smallest first.
$\frac{2}{5}$, 0.42, 0.041, $\frac{1}{3}$, 5%, 26%

Recurring decimals & surds

Changing recurring decimals into fractions

As recurring decimals are **rational numbers**, we can change them into fractions.

Example
Change $0.\dot{1}\dot{3}$ into a fraction in its simplest form.

Let $x = 0.131313...$ ①

then $100x = 13.131313...$ ②

(Multiply by 10^n, where n is the length of the recurring pattern. In this example it is two.)

❶ Subtract equation ① from equation ②.

$99x = 13$

This has the effect of making the recurring pattern disappear.

❷ Divide to leave x. $x = \frac{13}{99}$

❸ Since 13 is a prime number, this fraction is in its simplest form.

So $0.\dot{1}\dot{3} = \frac{13}{99}$

'Trick' method
There is a quick method of changing recurring decimals into fractions – the fraction has the repeating unit on the top and the same number of nines on the bottom. For example:

$0.\dot{2} = \frac{2}{9}$ $0.\dot{4}\dot{1} = \frac{41}{99}$ $0.\dot{1}\dot{2}\dot{3} = \frac{123}{999}$ $0.\dot{2}7\dot{1}\dot{3} = \frac{2713}{9999}$

Remember to simplify if possible. If you have a question where there are one or more numbers that are not repeated, extra care is needed.

Example
Change $0.2\dot{3}$ into a fraction.

$x = 0.2333...$ ①

$10x = 2.3333...$ ②   Multiply by 10.

$100x = 23.3333...$ ③   Multiply by 100.

Subtract equation ② from equation ③.

$90x = 21$ $x = \frac{21}{90} = \frac{7}{30}$

Number

Surds

Numbers written under a square root sign are called surds: $\sqrt{2}$, $\sqrt{3}$, $\sqrt{13}$, etc. Surds are **irrational numbers** because they cannot be written as fractions.

There are a few rules of surds you need to learn:

• $\sqrt{a} \times \sqrt{b} = \sqrt{ab}$

For example: $\sqrt{3} \times \sqrt{5} = \sqrt{15}$

• $\left(\sqrt{b}\right)^2 = \sqrt{b} \times \sqrt{b} = b$

For example: $\left(\sqrt{3}\right)^2 = 3$

• $\dfrac{\sqrt{a}}{\sqrt{b}} = \sqrt{\dfrac{a}{b}}$

For example: $\dfrac{\sqrt{10}}{\sqrt{2}} = \sqrt{\dfrac{10}{2}} = \sqrt{5}$

• $\left(a + \sqrt{b}\right)^2 = \left(a + \sqrt{b}\right)\left(a + \sqrt{b}\right)$
$= a^2 + 2a\sqrt{b} + \left(\sqrt{b}\right)^2 = a^2 + 2a\sqrt{b} + b$

• $\left(a + \sqrt{b}\right)\left(a - \sqrt{b}\right)$
$= a^2 - a\sqrt{b} + a\sqrt{b} - \left(\sqrt{b}\right)^2 = a^2 - b$

Examples
a) Simplify $\sqrt{200}$ Hint – look for square factors.

$\sqrt{200} = \sqrt{2} \times \sqrt{100}$
$= 10 \times \sqrt{2}$
$= 10\sqrt{2}$

b) Simplify $\left(4 - \sqrt{3}\right)^2$ Hint – see multiplying out two brackets on page 33.

$\left(4 - \sqrt{3}\right)^2 = \left(4 - \sqrt{3}\right)\left(4 - \sqrt{3}\right)$
$= 16 - 4\sqrt{3} - 4\sqrt{3} + \left(\sqrt{3}\right)^2$
$= 16 - 8\sqrt{3} + 3$
$= 19 - 8\sqrt{3}$

c) Simplify $\dfrac{1}{\sqrt{5}}$

$\dfrac{1}{\sqrt{5}} \times \dfrac{\sqrt{5}}{\sqrt{5}} = \dfrac{\sqrt{5}}{5}$ Multiply the top and bottom by $\sqrt{5}$.

This is known as '**rationalising the denominator**'.

Quick test

❶ Change the following recurring decimals into fractions. Write them in their simplest form.

  a) $0.\dot{1}\dot{5}$ b) $0.\dot{7}$ c) $0.2\dot{8}\dot{3}$

❷ Simplify: a) $\sqrt{75}$ b) $\sqrt{500}$ c) $\left(\sqrt{2} - 3\right)^2$ d) $6\left(\sqrt{2} + 3\right) - \sqrt{2}\left(2 + \sqrt{3}\right)$ e) $\dfrac{1}{\sqrt{3}}$

Ratio

Ratios

A ratio is used to compare two or more related quantities:
- 'Compared to' is replaced with two dots :
  For example, '16 boys compared to 20 girls' can be written as 16 : 20.
- To simplify ratios, divide both parts of the ratio by their highest common factor.
  For example, 16 : 20 = 4 : 5 [Divide both sides by 4.]

Example
Simplify the ratio 21 : 28.

21 : 28 = 3 : 4 [Divide both sides by 7.]

Here is another example:
Look at the flowers shown below. The ratio of red flowers to purple flowers can be written as:

$$10 : 4$$
$$= 5 : 2$$

The ratio of 5 : 2 is the same as $\frac{5}{7} : \frac{2}{7}$

In other words, for every 5 red flowers there are 2 purple flowers. To express the ratio 5 : 2 as the ratio $n : 1$, divide both sides by 2:

$$\div 2 \underset{= 2.5 : 1}{\overset{5 : 2}{\big(\quad\big)}} \div 2$$

Sharing a quantity in a given ratio

When sharing a quantity in a given ratio, follow these steps:
1. Add up the total parts.
2. Work out what one part is worth.
3. Work out what the other parts are worth.

Example
£20 000 is shared between Ewan and Leroy in the ratio 1 : 4. How much does each receive?

1 + 4 = 5 parts

5 parts = £20 000, so 1 part = $\frac{£20\,000}{5}$ = £4000

So, Ewan gets 1 × £4000 = £4000 and Leroy gets 4 × £4000 = £16 000

Best buys

Use unit amounts to decide which option is the better value for money.

Example
The same brand of coffee is sold in two different-sized jars. Which jar represents the better value for money?

Find the cost per gram for both jars.

100g costs 186p so 186 ÷ 100 = 1.86p per gram

250g costs 397p so 397 ÷ 250 = 1.588p per gram

Since the larger jar costs less per gram, it offers the better value for money.

For a non-calculator method, work out the cost of 50g for each jar:

100g = £1.86 so 50g = 186 ÷ 2 = 93p

250g = £3.97 so 50g = 397 ÷ 5 = 79.4p

Hence the larger jar is better value because it costs less per 50g.

Increasing and decreasing in a given ratio

The unitary method is useful when solving ratio problems:

❶ Divide to get one part.
❷ Multiply for each new part.

Examples

a) A photograph of length 9cm is to have its sides enlarged in the ratio 5 : 3. What is the length of the enlarged photograph?

❶ Divide 9cm by 3 to get 1 part.
   9 ÷ 3 = 3
❷ Multiply this by 5.
   5 × 3 = 15cm

So the length 9cm becomes 15cm on the enlarged photograph.

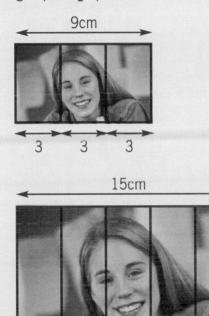

b) It took 8 people 6 days to build a wall. At the same rate, how long would it take 3 people?

Time for 8 people = 6 days
Time for 1 person = 8 × 6 = 48 days
(It takes 1 person longer to build the wall.)
3 people will take $\frac{1}{3}$ of the time taken by 1 person.
So time for 3 people = $\frac{48}{3}$ = 16 days

c) A recipe for 4 people needs 1600g of flour. How much flour is needed to make the recipe for 6 people?

❶ Divide 1600g by 4, so 400g for 1 person.
❷ Multiply by 6, so 6 × 400g = 2400g of flour is needed for 6 people.

> *When answering problems of the type shown here, always try to work out what a unit (or one) is worth. You should then be able to work out what any other value is worth.*

Quick test

❶ Write the following ratios in their simplest form.
   a) 12 : 15   **b)** 6 : 12   **c)** 25 : 10

❷ Three sisters share 60 sweets between them in the ratio 2 : 3 : 7. How many sweets does each sister receive? 🖩

❸ If 15 oranges cost £1.80, how much will 23 of the same oranges cost? 🖩

❹ A map is being enlarged in the ratio 12 : 7. If a road length was 21cm on the original map, what is the length of the road on the enlarged map? 🖩

Indices

Indices

An index (plural: indices) is sometimes known as a power. For example:
- 6^4 is read as '6 to the power of 4'.
  It means $6 \times 6 \times 6 \times 6$.
- 2^7 is read as '2 to the power of 7'.
  It means $2 \times 2 \times 2 \times 2 \times 2 \times 2 \times 2$.

The base has to be the same when the rules of indices are applied.

$$a^b$$

The base   The index or power

Rules of indices

You need to learn these rules of indices:
- When multiplying, add the powers.
  $4^7 \times 4^3 = 4^{7+3} = 4^{10}$
- When dividing, subtract the powers.
  $6^9 \div 6^4 = 6^{9-4} = 6^5$
- When raising one power to another, multiply the powers.
  $(7^2)^4 = 7^{2 \times 4} = 7^8$
- Anything raised to the power zero is 1, provided the number is not zero.
  $5^0 = 1$ $6^0 = 1$
  $2.7189^0 = 1$ $0^0 = $ undefined
- Anything to the power 1 is itself.
  $15^1 = 15$ $1923^1 = 1923$

All these rules also apply when the powers are negative. These examples demonstrate some of the rules above:
$$6^{-2} \times 6^{12} = 6^{-2+12} = 6^{10}$$
$$8^{-4} \times 8^{-3} = 8^{-4+-3} = 8^{-7}$$
$$(6^4)^{-2} = 6^{4 \times -2} = 6^{-8}$$
$$20^0 = 1$$

Negative and fractional powers

Negative powers
Turn a negative power **upside down** (take the reciprocal) to make the **power positive**.
In general, $a^{-n} = \dfrac{1}{a^n}$

For example:
$$4^{-2} = \frac{1}{4^2} = \frac{1}{16} \qquad \left(\frac{2}{3}\right)^{-2} = \left(\frac{3}{2}\right)^{2} = \frac{9}{4} \qquad 2x^{-3} = \frac{2}{x^3}$$

Fractional powers
Fractional powers mean **roots**.

In general, $a^{\frac{1}{m}} = \sqrt[m]{a}$

So...
- the power $\frac{1}{2}$ means square root $\sqrt{}$
- the power $\frac{1}{3}$ means cube root $\sqrt[3]{}$
- the power $\frac{1}{4}$ means fourth root $\sqrt[4]{}$, etc.

For example:
$$25^{\frac{1}{2}} = \sqrt{25} = 5 \qquad\qquad 8^{\frac{1}{3}} = \sqrt[3]{8} = 2$$
$$81^{\frac{1}{4}} = \sqrt[4]{81} = 3 \qquad\qquad \left(\frac{1}{8}\right)^{\frac{1}{3}} = \sqrt[3]{\frac{1}{8}} = \frac{1}{2}$$

Powers written as fractions
Sometimes, powers are written as fractions.
In general, $a^{\frac{n}{m}} = \left(\sqrt[m]{a}\right)^n$

For example:
$$8^{\frac{2}{3}} = \left(\sqrt[3]{8}\right)^2 = 2^2 = 4$$
$$64^{\frac{5}{6}} = \left(\sqrt[6]{64}\right)^5 = 2^5 = 32$$

If there is a negative fraction, remember to turn it upside down as well (take the reciprocal).
$$16^{-\frac{1}{2}} = \frac{1}{16^{\frac{1}{2}}} = \frac{1}{\sqrt{16}} = \frac{1}{4}$$
$$125^{-\frac{2}{3}} = \frac{1}{125^{\frac{2}{3}}} = \frac{1}{\left(\sqrt[3]{125}\right)^2} = \frac{1}{5^2} = \frac{1}{25}$$

Indices and algebra

The rules that apply with numbers also apply to algebra.

Laws of indices

$a^n \times a^m = a^{n+m}$

$a^n \div a^m = a^{n-m}$

$(a^n)^m = a^{n \times m}$

$a^0 = 1$

$a^1 = a$

$a^{-n} = \dfrac{1}{a^n}$

$a^{\frac{1}{m}} = \sqrt[m]{a}$

These examples demonstrate some of the laws above:

$4x^2 \times 3x^5 = 12x^7$

Note that the numbers are multiplied... ...but the powers of the same term are added.

$x^6 \times 4x^3 = 4x^9$

$12x^4 \div 3x^7 = 4x^{-3}$

Note that the numbers are divided... ...but the powers of the same term are subtracted.

$(7x^2)^2 = 49x^4$

$x^0 = 1$

$(2x^4)^3 = 8x^{12}$

$(2x)^{-3} = \dfrac{1}{(2x)^3} = \dfrac{1}{8x^3}$

Look at the following simplified expressions:

$$\frac{3x^7 \times 4x^9}{6x^4} = \frac{12x^{16}}{6x^4} = 2x^{12}$$

Work this out in two stages.

Take care when simplifying a fraction. Work it out in two stages.

$$\frac{12a^2b^3}{6a^3b^2} = \frac{2b}{a}$$

$$\frac{4a^4b^3}{2ab} = 2a^3b^2$$

$$\frac{15x^2y}{3xy} = 5x$$

$$\frac{14xy \times 2x^2y}{2x^2y^2} = \frac{28x^3y^2}{2x^2y^2} = 14x$$

$$\frac{6x^2y^4 \times 2xy}{3x^2y} = \frac{12x^3y^5}{3x^2y} = 4xy^4$$

$$\frac{5a^2b^2 \times 2a}{3a^3b^2} = \frac{10a^3b^2}{3a^3b^2} = \frac{10}{3}$$

Quick test

1. Simplify the following:
   a) $12^4 \times 12^8$
   b) $9^{-2} \times 9^{-4}$
   c) $18^6 \div 18^{-2}$
   d) $(4^2)^5$

2. Simplify the following:
   a) $x^4 \times x^9$
   b) $2x^6 \times 3x^7$
   c) $12x^4 \div 3x^2$
   d) $25x^9 \div 5x^{-2}$
   e) $\dfrac{5x^6 \times 4x^9}{10x^3}$

3. Evaluate the following:
   a) 4^0
   b) 1^{20}
   c) $(64)^{\frac{2}{3}}$
   d) 5^{-3}
   e) $144^{\frac{1}{2}}$
   f) $36^{-\frac{1}{2}}$

4. Simplify the following:
   a) $(4x)^{-2}$
   b) $(6x^2y^4)^{-2}$

Standard index form

Standard index form (standard form)

Standard index form (standard form) is used to write very large numbers or very small numbers in a simpler way.

When written in standard form, a number will be written as:

$$a \times 10^n$$

a must be at least 1 but not greater than 10, i.e. $1 \leqslant a < 10$.

n is the power of 10 by which you multiply (if n is positive), or divide (if n is negative).

Learn these rules:
- The front number (a) must always be at least 1 but less than 10.
- The power of 10, n:
  - If the number is 10 or more, n is **positive**.
  - If the number is less than 1, n is **negative**.

Big numbers

Example

Write 6 230 000 in standard form.

❶ Place the decimal point between the 6 and 2 to give 6.230 000 ($1 \leqslant 6.23 < 10$).

❷ Work out how many times you multiply by 10 to restore the number.

$$6\ 2\ 3\ 0\ 0\ 0\ 0 \qquad (n = 6)$$

❸ In standard form, $6\ 230\ 000 = 6.23 \times 10^6$

Other examples:
- $4371 = 4.371 \times 10^3$ in standard form.
- In June 2009, the UK national debt reached £798.8 billion, which is £798.8×10^{12} (a billion = 1×10^{12}). Written in standard form this is £7.988×10^{14}.

Small numbers

Example

Write 0.003 71 in standard form.

❶ Place the decimal point between the 3 and 7 to give 3.71 ($1 \leqslant 3.71 < 10$).

❷ Work out how many times you divide the number by 10.

$$0\ .\ 0\ 0\ 3\ 7\ 1 \qquad (n = 3)$$

❸ In standard form, $0.003\ 71 = 3.71 \times 10^{-3}$

Other examples:

$0.000\ 047\ 9 = 4.79 \times 10^{-5}$ in standard form.

$0.0046 = 4.6 \times 10^{-3}$ in standard form.

$0.56 = 5.6 \times 10^{-1}$ in standard form.

$0.049 = 4.9 \times 10^{-2}$ in standard form.

Calculations with standard form

On a non-calculator paper, the laws of indices can be used when multiplying and dividing numbers written in standard form. For example:

$(2.4 \times 10^{-4}) \times (3 \times 10^7)$

$= (2.4 \times 3) \times (10^{-4} \times 10^7)$

$= 7.2 \times 10^3$

$(12.4 \times 10^{-4}) \div (4 \times 10^7)$

$= (12.4 \div 4) \times (10^{-4} \div 10^7)$

$= 3.1 \times 10^{-11}$

When answering standard form questions, don't forget to write the answer in standard form, e.g.

$(2 \times 10^6) \times (6 \times 10^3) = (2 \times 6) \times (10^6 \times 10^3)$

$= 12 \times 10^9$

$= 1.2 \times 10^{10}$

Standard form and the calculator

It is important that you know how your calculator works. You can use the calculator to do complex calculations in standard form.

To key a number in standard form into the calculator, use the $\boxed{\text{EXP}}$ key.

(Some calculators use $\boxed{\text{EE}}$ or $\boxed{\times 10^x}$. Make sure that you check your calculator, as they vary greatly.)

For example, depending on the make of calculator, 6.23×10^6 could be keyed in as

$\boxed{6}$ $\boxed{.}$ $\boxed{2}$ $\boxed{3}$ $\boxed{\text{EXP}}$ $\boxed{6}$

4.93×10^{-5} can be keyed in as

$\boxed{4}$ $\boxed{.}$ $\boxed{9}$ $\boxed{3}$ $\boxed{\text{EXP}}$ $\boxed{5}$ $\boxed{+/-}$

Most calculators do not show standard form correctly on the display.

 means 7.632×10^9.

$\boxed{4.62^{-07}}$ means 4.62×10^{-7}.

Remember to put in the '$\times 10$' part if this has been left out.

Now look at this example:
$(2.6 \times 10^3) \times (8.9 \times 10^{12}) = 2.314 \times 10^{16}$
This would be keyed in as

$\boxed{2}$ $\boxed{.}$ $\boxed{6}$ $\boxed{\text{EXP}}$ $\boxed{3}$ $\boxed{\times}$ $\boxed{8}$ $\boxed{.}$ $\boxed{9}$ $\boxed{\text{EXP}}$ $\boxed{1}$ $\boxed{2}$ $\boxed{=}$

Check that for $(1.8 \times 10^6) \div (2.7 \times 10^{-3})$ ⟵ the answer is 6.7×10^8.

Some calculators may not put the answers in standard form.

Example

The mass of Pluto is approximately 1.29×10^{22} kg. The mass of Pluto is approximately 2.2×10^{-3} of the mass of the Earth. Work out the approximate mass of the Earth.

Mass of the Earth $= \dfrac{1.29 \times 10^{22}}{2.2 \times 10^{-3}}$

$= 5.86 \times 10^{24}$ kg (3 s.f.)

Earth   Pluto

A common mistake when answering standard form questions is reading a calculator display such as $\boxed{2.4^{07}}$ incorrectly and writing down 2.4^7 instead of 2.4×10^7.

Just key in as normal:

$\boxed{2}$ $\boxed{.}$ $\boxed{7}$ $\boxed{\text{EXP}}$ $\boxed{3}$ $\boxed{+/-}$

Number

Quick test

1. Write the following numbers in standard form.
   a) 630 000   b) 2730   c) 0.000 042 9   d) 0.000 000 63

2. Without a calculator work out the following, leaving your answers in standard form.
   a) $(2 \times 10^5) \times (3 \times 10^7)$ b) $(6.1 \times 10^{12}) \times (2 \times 10^{-4})$
   c) $(8 \times 10^9) \div (2 \times 10^6)$ d) $(6 \times 10^8) \div (2 \times 10^{-10})$

3. Work out the following on a calculator. Give your answers to 3 significant figures.
   a) $\dfrac{1.279 \times 10^9}{2.94 \times 10^{-2}}$ b) $(1.693 \times 10^4) \times (2.71 \times 10^{12})$

4. Calculate the following, giving your answer in standard form correct to 3 significant figures.
   $\dfrac{(3.72 \times 10^8) - (1.6 \times 10^4)}{3.81 \times 10^{-3}}$

Upper & lower bounds of measurement

Upper and lower bounds for a single measurement

If a length x (cm) is given as 6.2, correct to the nearest millimetre, then by the usual conventions of rounding:

$$6.15 \leqslant x < 6.25$$

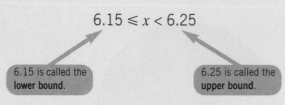

6.15 is called the **lower bound**.

6.25 is called the **upper bound**.

In general, the real value can be as much as half the unit above and below the rounded value.

For example, if $x = 6.23$ (correct to 2 d.p.) then the rounded unit is 0.01, so the real value can be anything between $6.225 \leqslant 6.23 < 6.235$

See page 79 for more information.

Calculations with measurements

When calculations are carried out using rounded values, then the calculated value lies between a maximum value and a minimum possible value.

Examples

a) i) A desk measures 62cm by 95cm. Work out the lower and upper bounds of the area of the desk.

Lower bound

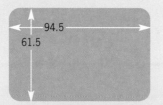
94.5
61.5

Lower bound of area
= 61.5 × 94.5 = 5811.75cm²

Upper bound

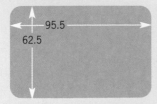
95.5
62.5

Upper bound of area
= 62.5 × 95.5 = 5968.75cm²

The rounded value = 62 × 95 = 5890cm²

ii) Work out the lower and upper bounds of the perimeter of the desk.

Lower bound of perimeter
= 2 × 61.5 + 2 × 94.5 = 312cm

Upper bound of perimeter
= 2 × 62.5 + 2 × 95.5 = 316cm

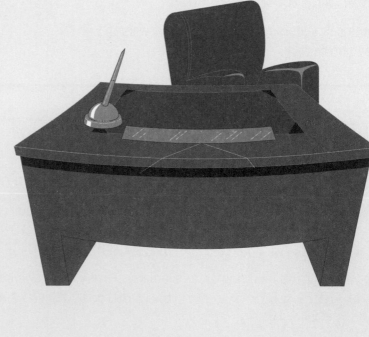

b) A toy has a mass of 120g and a volume of 60cm³ (both measurements are correct to the nearest 10 units). Calculate the lower and upper bounds for the density of the toy.

The upper and lower bounds of the mass are 125g and 115g; the upper and lower bounds of the volume are 65cm³ and 55cm³.

Lower bound of density $= \dfrac{115}{65} = 1.77$g/cm³ (2 d.p.)

Upper bound of density $= \dfrac{125}{55} = 2.27$g/cm³ (2 d.p.)

The process for working out the lower and upper bounds in multiplication and addition is quite straightforward. For subtraction and division, more care is needed. Here are a few tips:

- Finding a difference:

  Upper bound = $\dfrac{\text{upper bound of}}{\text{larger quantity}} - \dfrac{\text{lower bound of}}{\text{smaller quantity}}$

  Lower bound = $\dfrac{\text{lower bound of}}{\text{larger quantity}} - \dfrac{\text{upper bound of}}{\text{smaller quantity}}$

- Division:

  Upper bound = $\dfrac{\text{upper bound of quantity 1}}{\text{lower bound of quantity 2}}$

  Lower bound = $\dfrac{\text{lower bound of quantity 1}}{\text{upper bound of quantity 2}}$

This is a popular topic on exam papers. You must be careful on questions with division and subtraction, as it is easy to make a mistake. If in doubt, try all the different combinations (if you have time), but don't forget to cross out the ones you don't want!

Simon Hartshorne/iStockphoto/Thinkstock

Maximum percentage error

Maximum percentage error is found by using the following formula:

Percentage error $= \dfrac{\text{maximum error}}{\text{nominal value}} \times 100\%$

The 'nominal value' is the value that the quantity is supposed to have. You can think of it as the 'accurate value' (the value it would have if there was no error).

For the desk in the example on the previous page:
Maximum error:
5968.75 – 5890 = 78.75
5890 – 5811.75 = 78.25

Therefore, the upper bound of area provides the maximum error (78.75 compared with 78.25 with the lower bound).

Percentage error $= \dfrac{78.75}{5890} \times 100\% = 1.34\%$

Calculations are not always as straightforward as this.

Quick test

1. If $x = \dfrac{4}{y}$ and $y = 6.2$ (1 d.p.), calculate the upper and lower bounds of x. 🔢

2. If $h = ab$, $a = 2.7$ (1 d.p.) and $b = 20$ (to the nearest whole number), calculate the upper and lower bounds of h. 🔢

Practice questions

Use these questions to test your progress. Check your answers on page 110. You may wish to answer these questions on a separate piece of paper so that you can show full working out, which you will be expected to do in the exam.

1 Mrs Patel inherits £55000. She divides the money between her children in the ratio 3 : 3 : 5. How much does the child with the largest share receive?

2 Work these out on your calculator, giving your answers to 3 significant figures. 🖩

  a) $\dfrac{4.2 \times (3.6 + 5.1)}{2 - 1.9}$ b) $\dfrac{3.8 + 4.6}{2.9 \times 4.1}$

3 Show how you would estimate the answer to this expression without using a calculator. Work out the estimate. $\dfrac{8.7 + 9.02}{0.2 \times 48}$

4 a) Express 60 as a product of its prime factors.

  b) Find the lowest common multiple (LCM) of 60 and 150.

5 Toothpaste is sold in three different-sized tubes.
  50ml = £1.24   75ml = £1.96   100ml = £2.42
  Which of the tubes of toothpaste is the best value for money? You must show full working in order to justify your answer. 🖩

6 The price of a CD player has been reduced by 15% in a sale. It now costs £320. What was the original price? 🖩

7 A car was bought for £9000. Each year it depreciated in value by 15%. What was the car worth two years later? 🖩

8 Find, to the nearest penny, the compound interest earned when £4500 is invested for three years at 3.2% per annum. 🖩

9 The price of a television has risen from £350 to £420. Work out the percentage increase in the price. 🖩

10 Write these numbers in standard form.

   a) 2670000   **b)** 4270   **c)** 0.03296   **d)** 0.027

---

11 Work out the answers to these questions, giving your answer in standard form.

   a) $(2 \times 10^9) \times (6 \times 10^{12})$ _____

   b) $(8 \times 10^9) \div (4 \times 10^{-2})$ _____

12 Write these recurring decimals as fractions.

   a) $0.\dot{4}$ **b)** $0.\dot{2}\dot{1}$ **c)** $0.\dot{2}3\dot{4}$ **d)** $0.2\dot{7}$

---

13 Simplify the following:

   a) $\sqrt{12}$ **b)** $\sqrt{150}$ **c)** $\sqrt{200}$ **d)** $\sqrt{6}\left(\sqrt{3} - 2\right)$ **e)** $\sqrt{3} \times \sqrt{75}$

---

14 A television costs £320, including VAT at 17.5%. The rate of VAT is reduced to 15%. What is the price of the television now? 🖩

---

15 The number of bacteria, N, after t hours is given by $N = 100 \times 5^{2t}$. How many bacteria are there after three hours? 🖩

---

16 Samuel cycles 1250m in 95s. Assuming that the time is measured to the nearest second and the distance to the nearest 10 metres, find the upper and lower bounds of Samuel's average speed in metres per second. 🖩

---

17 The area of a circle is 142cm², correct to 3 s.f. Find the upper and lower bounds of the radius of the circle. (Hint: πr^2 is the formula for the area of a circle). 🖩

---

18 Evaluate the following:

   a) $64^{\frac{1}{3}}$ _____   **b)** $8^{\frac{2}{3}}$ _____   **c)** 6^{-2} _____   **d)** $49^{\frac{1}{2}}$ _____

   e) $25^{-\frac{1}{2}}$ _____   **f)** $(4)^{-2}$ _____   **g)** $\left(\frac{5}{7}\right)^{-2}$ _____

19 Sarah says, '$\sqrt{2}$ is a rational number.' Is Sarah correct? Give a reason for your answer.

---

20 Write down whether each of the following numbers are rational or irrational.

   a) π **b)** $\sqrt{81}$ **c)** $\sqrt{20}$ **d)** $\left(3 - \sqrt{2}\right)^2$ **e)** $\left(\sqrt{3} + 5\right)\left(\sqrt{3} - 5\right)$

How well did you do?

0–6 **Try again**   7–10 **Getting there**   11–15 **Good work**   16–20 **Excellent!**

Algebra 1

Algebraic conventions

Make sure you understand the following conventions of algebra:

- A **term** is a collection of numbers, letters and brackets, all multiplied together.
- Terms are separated by + and – signs. Each term has a + or – attached to the front of it.

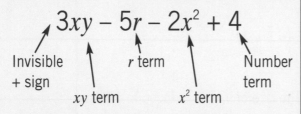

$$3xy - 5r - 2x^2 + 4$$

Invisible
+ sign

xy term

r term

x^2 term

Number term

- An algebraic expression must contain at least one letter (or non-numeric symbol).
- $3 \times a$ is written without the multiplication sign as $3a$.

$a + a + a = 3a$

$a \times a \times 2 = 2a^2$, not $(2a)^2$

$a \times a \times a = a^3$, not $3a$

$a \times b \times 2 = 2ab$

Collecting like terms

Expressions can be simplified by collecting **like terms**. Only collect the terms if their letters and powers are identical. For example:

$4a + 2a = 6a$

$3a^2 + 6a^2 - 4a^2 = 5a^2$

$4a + 6b - 3a + 2b = a + 8b$

> Add the *a* terms together, then the terms with *b*. Remember *a* means $1a$.

$9a + 4b$

> Cannot be simplified since there are no like terms.

$3xy + 2yx = 5xy$

> Remember *xy* means the same as *yx*.

Expressions and substituting

$p + 3$ is an **expression**.

$y = p + 3$ is a **formula**. The value of y depends on the value of p.

Replacing a letter with a number is called **substitution**. When substituting...

- write out the expressions first and then replace the letters with the values given
- pay attention to the order of operations – BIDMAS.

Examples

Using $a = 3$ and $b = -2$, find the values of these expressions:

a) $2a^2 + 4$

$2a^2 + 4 = 2 \times 3^2 + 4$
$\quad\quad\quad = 2 \times 9 + 4$
$\quad\quad\quad = 18 + 4$
$\quad\quad\quad = 22$

> Remember to show the substitutions and the rules of BIDMAS.

b) $b^2 - 1$

$b^2 - 1 = (-2)^2 - 1$
$\quad\quad\quad = (-2 \times -2) - 1$
$\quad\quad\quad = 4 - 1$
$\quad\quad\quad = 3$

> Be careful when substituting negative numbers.

c) $3b^3 + 2$

$3b^3 + 2 = 3 \times (-2)^3 + 2$
$\quad\quad\quad = 3 \times (-8) + 2$
$\quad\quad\quad = -24 + 2$
$\quad\quad\quad = -22$

> $(-2)^3$ means $-2 \times -2 \times -2 = -8$

When substituting into an expression or a formula, you must show each step of your working out. By showing your substitutions, you will obtain method marks even if you get the final answer wrong.

Multiplying out brackets

Multiplying out brackets helps to simplify algebraic expressions. The term outside the brackets multiplies each separate term inside the brackets. For example:

$3(2x + 5) = 6x + 15$ — $3 \times 2x = 6x, 3 \times 5 = 15$

$a(3a - 4) = 3a^2 - 4a$

$b(2a + 3b - c) = 2ab + 3b^2 - bc$

If the term outside the bracket is negative, all of the signs of the terms inside the bracket are changed when multiplying out. For example:

$-4(2x + 3) = -8x - 12$

$-2(4 - 3x) = -8 + 6x$

To simplify expressions, first expand the brackets then collect like terms.

Examples

a) Expand and simplify $2(x - 3) + x(x + 4)$.
$= 2x - 6 + x^2 + 4x$ — Multiply out the brackets. Collect like terms.
$= x^2 + 6x - 6$

b) Expand and simplify $6y - 2(y - 3)$.
$= 6y - 2y + 6$ — Take care when multiplying by a negative number.
$= 4y + 6$

An **identity** connects expressions involving unspecified numbers. An identity always remains true, no matter what numerical values replace the letter symbols. It has an $\equiv$ sign. For example, the following is true whatever the value of x:

$3(x + 2) \equiv 3x + 6$

💡 *If you are asked to 'expand' brackets it just means multiply them out. When you have finished multiplying out the brackets, simplify by collecting like terms in order to pick up the final mark.*

Multiplication of two brackets

Each term in the first bracket is multiplied by each term in the second; simplify by collecting like terms.

Examples

a) Expand and simplify $(x + 2)(x + 3)$.
$= x(x + 3) + 2(x + 3)$
$= x^2 + 3x + 2x + 6$
$= x^2 + 5x + 6$

b) Expand and simplify $(2x + 4)(3x - 2)$.
$= 2x(3x - 2) + 4(3x - 2)$
$= 6x^2 - 4x + 12x - 8$
$= 6x^2 + 8x - 8$

c) Expand and simplify $(x + y)^2$.
$\equiv (x + y)(x + y)$
$\equiv x(x + y) + y(x + y)$
$\equiv x^2 + xy + xy + y^2$
$\equiv x^2 + 2xy + y^2$ — This is an identity; it is true for all values of x.

💡 *A common error is to think that $(a + b)^2$ means $a^2 + b^2$.*

Quick test

1 Simplify these expressions by collecting like terms.
  a) $5a + 2a + 3a$ **b)** $6a - 3b + 4b + 2a$
  c) $5x - 3x + 7x - 2y + 6y$ **d)** $3xy^2 - 2x^2y + 6x^2y - 8xy^2$

2 If $x = 4$, find the value of...
  a) $x^2 - 4$ **b)** $2x^3$ **c)** $\dfrac{3x^2}{8}$

3 Multiply out the brackets and simplify where possible.
  a) $3(x + 2)$ **b)** $2(x + y)$ **c)** $-3(2x + 4)$
  d) $(x + 3)(x + 5)$ **e)** $(y - 4)(y - 3)$ **f)** $(a + 2)^2$

4 If $v = u + at$, find v if $a = -10$, $u = 25$ and $t = 4$.

Algebra 2

Factorisation (putting brackets in)

Factorisation is the reverse of expanding brackets. An expression is put into brackets by taking out **common factors**. For example:

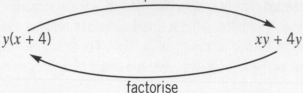

To **factorise** $xy + 4y$, follow these steps:

① Recognise that y is a factor of each term.

② Take out the common factor.

③ The expression is completed inside the bracket, so that the result is equivalent to $xy + 4y$ when multiplied out.

Examples

Factorise the following:

a) $\quad 5x^2 + x$

$\quad = x(5x + 1)$

b) $\quad 4x^2 + 8x$

$\quad = 4x(x + 2)$

c) $\quad 5x^3 + 15x^4$

$\quad = 5x^3(1 + 3x)$

Factorising can be useful when simplifying algebraic fractions.

Example

Simplify $\dfrac{5x + 15}{x + 3}$

$$\frac{5x + 15}{x + 3} = \frac{5(x + 3)^1}{(x + 3)^1} = 5$$

Factorisation of a quadratic

Two brackets are obtained when a quadratic expression of the type $x^2 + bx + c$ is factorised.

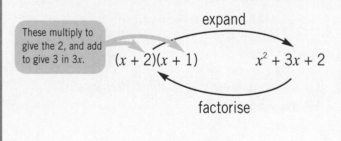

These multiply to give the 2, and add to give 3 in $3x$.

Examples

Factorise the following expressions.

a) $\quad x^2 + 5x - 6$

$\quad = (x - 1)(x + 6)$

b) $\quad x^2 - 6x + 8$

$\quad = (x - 2)(x - 4)$

c) $\quad x^2 - 25$

$\quad = (x - 5)(x + 5)$

Example **c)** is known as the 'difference of two squares'. In general, $x^2 - a^2 = (x - a)(x + a)$

Further factorising

Some quadratic equations have coefficients in front of x^2 greater than 1.

Example

Factorise $12x^2 - 13x + 1$.

① Multiply the coefficient of x^2 by the constant term.

$\quad 12 \times 1 = 12$

② Find two numbers whose product is +12 and whose sum is -13.

$\quad -12 \times -1 = 12$

$\quad -12 + -1 = -13$

③ Write $-13x$ as $-12x - x$.

$\quad 12x^2 - 12x - x + 1$

④ Factorise by grouping; the bracketed term must be the same.

$\quad 12x(x - 1) - 1(x - 1)$

⑤ $(x - 1)$ is a common factor.

$\quad (x - 1)(12x - 1)$

Hence: $12x^2 - 13x + 1 = (x - 1)(12x - 1)$

Algebraic fractions

When working with algebraic fractions, the rules are the same as for ordinary fractions.

Addition and subtraction
Always find a common denominator (the same bottom line) and then correct the numerators. Simplify by multiplying out the numerator and collecting like terms. For example:

$$\frac{x+2}{x-1} + \frac{3}{x}$$

$$= \frac{x(x+2)}{x(x-1)} + \frac{3(x-1)}{x(x-1)}$$

$$= \frac{x^2 + 2x + 3x - 3}{x(x-1)}$$

$$= \frac{x^2 + 5x - 3}{x(x-1)}$$

$$\frac{5}{(x+2)} - \frac{2}{(x-3)}$$

$$= \frac{5(x-3) - 2(x+2)}{(x+2)(x-3)}$$

$$= \frac{5x - 15 - 2x - 4}{(x+2)(x-3)}$$

$$= \frac{3x - 19}{(x+2)(x-3)}$$

Multiplication
Simply multiply the numerators together and the denominators together and cancel if possible. For example:

$$\frac{3p^2 q}{r^2 s} \times \frac{2rs}{9pq^2}$$

$$= \frac{2p}{3qr}$$

$$\frac{6(x+2)}{(x-1)} \times \frac{(x+1)}{12(x+2)(x+3)}$$

$$= \frac{6\cancel{(x+2)}^{1}}{(x-1)} \times \frac{(x+1)}{\cancel{12}_{2}\cancel{(x+2)}(x+3)}$$

$$= \frac{(x+1)}{2(x-1)(x+3)}$$

Division
When dividing algebraic fractions, turn the second fraction upside down (i.e. take the reciprocal), then multiply and cancel if possible. For example:

$$\frac{3x-3}{x^2 - 5x + 4} \div \frac{5x + 10}{x^2 - 2x - 8}$$

$$= \frac{3x-3}{x^2 - 5x + 4} \times \frac{x^2 - 2x - 8}{5x + 10}$$

> Take the reciprocal.

$$= \frac{3\cancel{(x-1)}^{1}}{_{1}\cancel{(x-1)}(x-4)_{1}} \times \frac{^{1}\cancel{(x-4)}(x+2)^{1}}{5\cancel{(x+2)}_{1}}$$

> Factorise first, then cancel.

$$= \frac{3}{5}$$

$$\frac{5x + 10}{x^2 + 5x + 6} \div \frac{x^2 + x - 6}{x^2 - 4}$$

$$= \frac{5x + 10}{x^2 + 5x + 6} \times \frac{x^2 - 4}{x^2 + x - 6}$$

$$= \frac{5(x+2)}{(x+2)(x+3)} \times \frac{(x-2)(x+2)}{(x-2)(x+3)}$$

> Factorise first, then cancel.

$$= \frac{5(x+2)}{(x+3)^2}$$

Quick test

1. Factorise the following expressions.
   a) $3x + 9$
   b) $5y - 15$
   c) $12x^2 - 6x$
   d) $x^2 - 5x - 6$
   e) $x^2 - 3x + 2$
   f) $x^2 - 16$
   g) $2x^2 - 7x + 3$
   h) $6x^2 + 5x + 1$

2. Simplify the following algebraic fractions.
   a) $\frac{2}{(x+2)} + \frac{3}{(x-1)}$
   b) $\frac{4(s-1)}{3(s+2)} \times \frac{(s+2)^2}{8(s-3)}$
   c) $\frac{8(a^2 - b^2)}{3(a+2)} \div \frac{4(a-b)}{27(a+1)}$

Equations 1

Solving linear equations of the form $ax + b = cx + d$

An **equation** involves finding at least one unknown value that has to be worked out.

The trick with **linear equations** is to get all the x terms together on one side of the equals sign and the numbers on the other side.

Example

Solve $5x - 9 = 12 - 4x$.

$$9x - 9 = 12 \quad \longleftarrow \text{Add } 4x \text{ to both sides.}$$
$$9x = 21 \quad \longleftarrow \text{Add 9 to both sides.}$$
$$x = \tfrac{21}{9} = 2\tfrac{1}{3}$$

If in the exam you do not know that $\tfrac{21}{9} = 2\tfrac{1}{3}$, leave it as $\tfrac{21}{9}$ to obtain full marks!

Solving linear equations with brackets

Just because an equation has brackets, don't be put off. The method is just the same as for the other equations once the brackets have been multiplied out.

Examples

a) Solve $3(x - 2) = 2(x + 6)$.

$$3x - 6 = 2x + 12 \quad \text{Multiply out the brackets first.}$$
$$x - 6 = 12$$
$$x = 18$$

b) Solve $5(x - 2) + 6 = 3(x - 4) + 10$.

$$5x - 10 + 6 = 3x - 12 + 10$$
$$5x - 4 = 3x - 2$$
$$2x = 2$$
$$x = 1$$

Solving quadratic equations

Make sure the **quadratic equation** is equal to zero. Then factorise the quadratic equation.

Examples

a) Solve $x^2 - 5x = 0$. $\quad$ *x is a common factor.*

$$x(x - 5) = 0$$
Either $x = 0$,
or $x - 5 = 0$, i.e. $x = 5$

b) Solve $x^2 - 3x = 10$.

$$x^2 - 3x - 10 = 0 \quad \text{Make it equal to zero, then factorise.}$$
$$(x + 2)(x - 5) = 0$$
Either $(x + 2) = 0$, i.e. $x = -2$,
or $(x - 5) = 0$, i.e. $x = 5$

c) Solve $3x^2 - x - 4 = 0$. $\quad$ *Product: $3 \times \text{-}4 = \text{-}12$ Sum: $3 + \text{-}4 = \text{-}1$*

$$3x^2 + 3x - 4x - 4 = 0$$
$$3x(x + 1) - 4(x + 1) = 0$$
$$(x + 1)(3x - 4) = 0$$
Either $x + 1 = 0$, i.e. $x = -1$,
or $3x - 4 = 0$, i.e. $x = \tfrac{4}{3}$

Completing the square

Completing the square is the method used when quadratic equations are expressed in the form $(x + a)^2 + b = 0$. Follow these steps:

❶ Rearrange the equation in the form $ax^2 + bx + c = 0$. If a is not 1, then divide the whole equation by a.

❷ Write the equation in the form $(x + \frac{b}{2})^2$ Notice that the constant in the bracket is always half the value of b.

❸ Multiply out the brackets, compare to the original and adjust by adding or subtracting an extra amount.

The minimum value of $(x + a)^2 + b$ occurs at b since $(x + a)^2 \geqslant 0$.

Example

Express $x^2 - 4x + 1 = 0$ as a completed square and, hence, solve it.

❶ $x^2 - 4x + 1 = 0$

> This is already in the form $ax^2 + bx + c = 0$ and $a = 1$.

❷ $(x - 2)^2$

> Half of -4 is -2.

❸ $(x - 2)^2 - x^2 - 4x + 1$

> Multiply out the brackets and now compare to the original $x^2 - 4x + 1$. To make $x^2 - 4x + 4$ like the original we need to subtract 3. Now we need to solve the equation.

❹ So $(x - 2)^2 - 3 = 0$

$(x - 2)^2 = 3$

$(x - 2) = \pm \sqrt{3}$

> Leave your answer in surd form.

So $x = \sqrt{3} + 2$, or $x = -\sqrt{3} + 2$

Using equations to solve problems

The following example will help you to understand how equations can be used to solve problems.

Example

The perimeter of the triangle is 20cm.
Work out the value of x and hence find the length of the three sides.

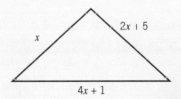

$x + (2x + 5) + (4x + 1) = 20$

$7x + 6 = 20$

$7x = 20 - 6$

$7x = 14$

$x = \dfrac{14}{7} = 2$

> The perimeter is found by adding the lengths together. Collect like terms and solve the equation as before.

So the lengths of the sides are
2 (= x), 9 (= $2x + 5$) and 9 (= $4x + 1$).

> 💡 *Solving equations is a very common topic at GCSE. Try to work through them in a logical way, always showing full working out. If you have time, check your answer by substituting it back into the equation to see if it works.*

Quick test

❶ Solve the following equations.

    a) $2x - 3 = 9$ **b)** $4x + 2 = 20$ **c)** $5x + 3 = 2x + 9$

    d) $6x - 1 = 15 + 2x$ **e)** $3(x + 2) = x + 4$ **f)** $2(x - 1) = 12(x + 1)$

    g) $x^2 + 4x - 5 = 0$ **h)** $x^2 - 5x + 6 = 0$ **i)** $3x^2 - 7x + 2 = 0$

    j) $2x^2 + 5x + 2 = 0$

Equations 2

Simultaneous equations

Two equations with two unknowns are called **simultaneous equations**. They can be solved in several ways. Solving equations simultaneously involves finding values for the letters that will make both equations work.

Graphical method

The points at which any two graphs intersect represent the simultaneous solutions of those equations.

Example

Solve the simultaneous equations
$y = 2x - 1$ and $x + y = 5$.

❶ Draw the two graphs.

$y = 2x - 1$	If $x = 0$, $y = -1$
	If $y = 0$, $x = \frac{1}{2}$
$x + y = 5$	If $x = 0$, $y = 5$
	If $x = 5$, $y = 0$

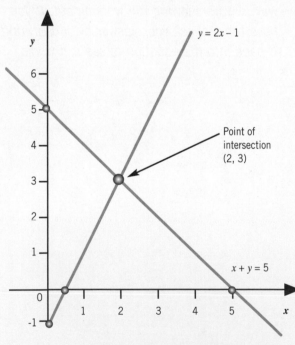

Point of intersection (2, 3)

❷ At the point of intersection $x = 2$ and $y = 3$.

Elimination method

If the **coefficient** of one of the letters is the same in both equations, then that letter may be eliminated by subtracting the equations.

The coefficient is the number a letter is multiplied by, e.g. the coefficient of -2x is -2.

Example

Solve simultaneously $2x + 3y = 6$ and $x + y = 1$.

❶ Label the equations ① and ②.
$$2x + 3y = 6 \quad ①$$
$$x + y = 1 \quad ②$$

❷ Since no coefficients match, multiply equation ② by 2. Rename it equation ③.
$$2x + 3y = 6 \quad ① \Big) \times 2$$
$$2x + 2y = 2 \quad ③$$

❸ The coefficients of x in equations ① and ③ are the same. Subtract equation ③ from equation ① and then solve the remaining equation.

$$2x + 3y = 6$$
$$\underline{2x + 2y = 2}$$
$$0x + y = 4$$
$$\therefore y = 4$$

❹ Substitute the value $y = 4$ into equation ① or equation ②. Solve the resulting equation to find x.
$$x + 4 = 1$$
$$x = 1 - 4$$
$$x = -3$$

❺ Check in equation ①.
$$(2 \times -3) + (3 \times 4) = 6$$
$$-6 + 12 = 6 ✔$$

The solution is $x = -3$, $y = 4$.

> *Simultaneous equations can be difficult to master. Try to learn the steps outlined here and practise lots of examples. Use the check at the end to make sure that you have the correct answers.*

> *Remember...*
> - *to eliminate terms with opposite signs, add the equations*
> - *to eliminate terms with the same signs, subtract the equations.*

Solving cubic equations by trial and improvement

Trial and improvement gives an approximate solution to **cubic equations**.

Example

The equation $x^3 - 5x = 10$ has a solution between 2 and 3. Find this solution to 2 decimal places.

Draw a table to help.
Substitute different values of x into $x^3 - 5x$.

x	$x^3 - 5x$	Comment
2.5	3.125	Too small
2.8	7.952	Too small
2.9	9.889	Too small
2.95	10.922375	Too big
2.94	10.712184	Too big
2.91	10.092171	Too big

At this stage the solution is trapped between 2.90 and 2.91. Checking the middle value, $x = 2.905$, gives $x^3 - 5x = 9.99036...$ which is too small.

```
|
2.90                2.905              2.91
(too small)         (too small)       (too big)
```

Because $x = 2.905$ is too small, the solution is closer to 2.91, correct to 2 decimal places.

💡 *Make sure you write down the solution of x, not the answer to $x^3 - 5x$.*

Trial and improvement can also be used to locate a root of an equation. The root of a graph is the point where the graph crosses the x-axis, that is when $y = 0$. The value of y changes from being positive to negative on either side of the root.

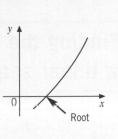

For example, for the curve $y = x^3 - 3x - 5$, a root lies between $x = 2.27$ and $x = 2.28$, since the value of y changes from negative to positive in this interval.

When $x = 2.27$, $y = 2.27^3 - (3 \times 2.27) - 5$
$$y = -0.1129$$

When $x = 2.28$, $y = 2.28^3 - (3 \times 2.28) - 5$
$$y = 0.0123$$

When $x = 2.275$, $y = 2.275^3 - (3 \times 2.275) - 5$
$$y = -0.0505$$

Hence the root is $x = 2.28$, correct to 2 decimal places.

Algebra

Quick test

1. Solve the following pairs of simultaneous equations.
   a) $4x + 7y = 10$
      $2x + 3y = 3$
   b) $3a - 5b = 1$ ① Hint – multiply equation ① by 2 and equation ② by 3.
      $2a + 3b = 7$ ②

2. The diagram shows the graphs of the equations
   $x + y = 2$ and $y = x - 4$.
   Use the diagram to solve the simultaneous equations
   $x + y = 2$
   $y = x - 4$

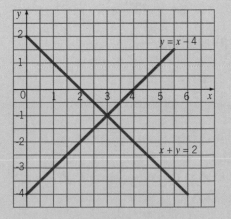

3. The equation $y^3 + y = 40$ has a solution between 3 and 4. Find this solution to 1 decimal place by using a method of trial and improvement. 🖩

Number patterns & sequences

Finding the nth term of a linear sequence

A **sequence** is a list of numbers. There is usually a relationship between the numbers. Each number in the list is called a **term**.

For example, the odd numbers form a sequence 1, 3, 5, 7, 9, 11, ..., in which the terms have a **common difference** of 2.

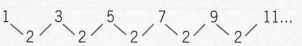

The nth term gives an expression for the term in the nth position.

The nth term of a linear sequence is of the form $an + b$.

Example

Find an expression for the nth term of this sequence: 3, 5, 7, 9, ...

❶ Find the common difference; this is **a**.
Difference = 2, so **a** = 2.
So the nth term = $2n + b$.

Term	1	2	3	4 . . . . n
Number in sequence	3	5	7	9 . . . .

❷ Now substitute the value of $n = 1$ and the number in the sequence; in this case it is 3.

nth term = $2n + b$
$3 = 2 \times 1 + b$
$3 = 2 + b$
$3 - 2 = b$
$b = 1$
nth term is $2n + 1$

❸ Check when $n = 2$ $\quad 2 \times 2 + 1 = 5$
Number in sequence is 5 so the nth term is $2n + 1$.

Finding the nth term of a quadratic sequence

For a quadratic sequence, the first differences are not constant but the second differences are.

The nth term takes the form
$U_n = an^2 + bn + c$
where b and/or c may be zero.

Example

Find the nth term of 3, 9, 19, 33, ...

Term (U_n)	1	2	3	4
Number	3	9	19	33
1st difference		6	10	14
2nd difference			4	4

a is found by dividing the second difference by 2.

To find the values of a, b and c, substitute into $2n^2 + bn + c$:

If $n = 1$ $\quad 2(1)^2 + b(1) + c = 3$
$\qquad\qquad\qquad\qquad b + c = 1$
If $n = 2$ $\quad 2(2)^2 + b(2) + c = 9$
$\qquad\qquad\qquad\quad 8 + 2b + c = 9$
$\qquad\qquad\qquad\qquad 2b + c = 1$
Hence $b = 0$ and $c = 1$. The nth term is $2n^2 + 1$.

Quick test

❶ Write down the next two terms in each of these sequences.
a) 5, 7, 9, 11, ___ , ___
b) 1, 4, 9, 16, ___ , ___
c) 12, 10, 8, 6, ___ , ___

❷ Write down the nth term of each of these sequences.
a) 5, 7, 9, 11, ...
b) 2, 5, 8, 11, ...
c) 6, 10, 14, 18, ...
d) 8, 6, 4, 2, ...

Inequalities

The four inequality symbols

Inequalities are solved in a similar way to equations.
> means 'greater than'
< means 'less than'
≥ means 'greater than or equal to'
≤ means 'less than or equal to'
So $x > 3$ and $3 < x$ both say 'x is greater than 3'.

Dividing by a negative number reverses the
direction of the inequality sign:
$$-2x < 6$$
$$x > \frac{6}{-2}$$
$$x > -3$$

Examples
Solve the following inequalities.

a) $2x + 1 < 11$

$$2x < 11 - 1$$
$$2x < 10$$
$$x < \frac{10}{2}$$
$$x < 5$$

The solution of this inequality can be represented
on a number line:

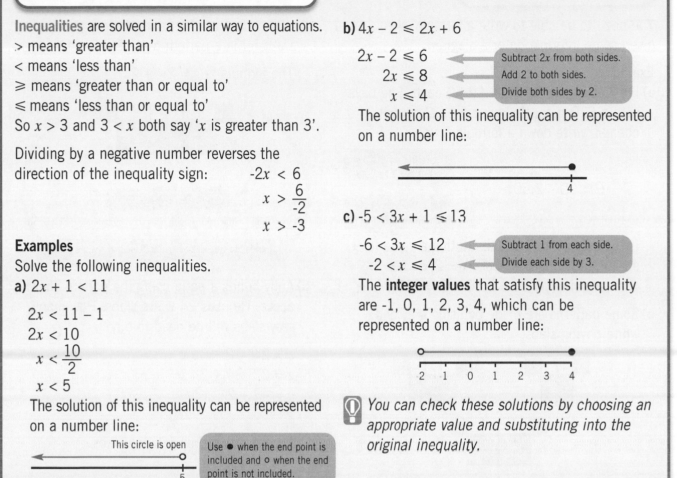

This circle is open

Use ● when the end point is included and ○ when the end point is not included.

b) $4x - 2 \leqslant 2x + 6$

$$2x - 2 \leqslant 6 \quad \longleftarrow \text{Subtract } 2x \text{ from both sides.}$$
$$2x \leqslant 8 \quad \longleftarrow \text{Add 2 to both sides.}$$
$$x \leqslant 4 \quad \longleftarrow \text{Divide both sides by 2.}$$

The solution of this inequality can be represented
on a number line:

c) $-5 < 3x + 1 \leqslant 13$

$$-6 < 3x \leqslant 12 \quad \longleftarrow \text{Subtract 1 from each side.}$$
$$-2 < x \leqslant 4 \quad \longleftarrow \text{Divide each side by 3.}$$

The **integer values** that satisfy this inequality
are -1, 0, 1, 2, 3, 4, which can be
represented on a number line:

💡 *You can check these solutions by choosing an
appropriate value and substituting into the
original inequality.*

Graphs of inequalities

The graph of an equation such as $y = 3$ is a line,
whereas the graph of the inequality $y < 3$ is a
region that has the line $y = 3$ as its **boundary**.

How to show the region for given inequalities:
- Draw the boundary lines first.
- For **strict** inequalities > and <, the boundary line
  is not included and is shown as a dotted line.
- It is often easier with several inequalities to
  shade out the unwanted regions, so that the
  solution is shown **unshaded** (as in the example).

For example, the
diagram shows
unshaded the region
$x > 1$, $x + y \leqslant 4$, $y \geqslant 0$.

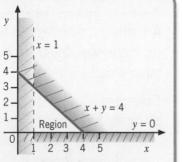

Graphical inequalities are used in an area of
mathematics called linear programming. Linear
programming is used for solving allocation problems
and is widely used in businesses and organisations.

Quick test

① Solve the following inequalities.
   a) $2x - 3 < 9$ **b)** $5x + 1 \geqslant 21$ **c)** $1 \leqslant 3x - 2 \leqslant 7$ **d)** $1 \leqslant 5x + 2 < 12$

Algebra

Formulae

Writing formulae

You need to be able to write a formula when given some information or a diagram.

Examples

a) Frances buys x books at £2.50 each. She pays with a £20 note. If she receives C pounds change, write down a formula for C.

$C = 20 - 2.50x$

> Notice that no £ signs are put in the formula.

> This is the amount of money she spent.

If in doubt, check by substituting a value for x, e.g.: if she bought 2 books $x = 2$, so her change would be $20 - 2.50 \times 2 = £15.00$ ✔

b) Some patterns are made by using grey and white paving slabs.

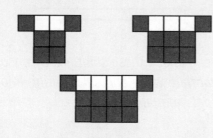

i) Write a formula for the number of grey paving slabs (g) in a pattern that uses w white ones.

The formula is $g = 2w + 2$.

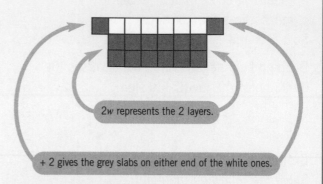

> $2w$ represents the 2 layers.

> + 2 gives the grey slabs on either end of the white ones.

ii) Andy builds a patio using the pattern shown above. He uses 24 white slabs. How many grey slabs will he need to buy?

$g = 2w + 2$
$g = 2 \times 24 + 2$
$g = 48 + 2$
$g = 50$

Andy needs to buy 50 grey slabs.

Using formulae

A formula describes the relationship between two (or more) variables. A formula must have an equals sign (=) in it.

Examples

a) James hires a van. There is a standing charge of £17 and then it costs £21 per day. How much does it cost for...

i) 6 days?
$17 + (21 \times 6) = £143$

ii) y days?
$17 + (21 \times y) = £(17 + 21y)$

iii) Write a formula for the total hire cost, C.
$C = 17 + 21y$

> This is a formula that works out the cost of hiring the van for any number of days.

b) A rule for working out the average carbon dioxide emission from a coach is given by:

$$\text{Carbon dioxide emission} = \text{Distance travelled (km)} \times 0.17$$

If C stands for the carbon dioxide emission in grams and d stands for the distance travelled in kilometres...

i) write down a formula for the total carbon dioxide emission, C.
$C = d \times 0.17$ or $C = 0.17d$

ii) work out the carbon dioxide emission for a coach that travels a distance of 28km.
$C = 28 \times 0.17$
$= 4.76$ grams

Substituting into formulae

Replacing a letter with a number is called **substitution**. Substituting into formulae is similar to substituting into expressions. When substituting...
- replace the letters in the formula with the value given
- work out the value on your calculator. Use bracket keys where possible and pay attention to the order of operations.

Example

The formula $C = \dfrac{5(F - 32)}{9}$ is used to change the temperature from degrees Fahrenheit (F) into degrees centigrade (C). Work out the value of C when $F = -12$.

$C = \dfrac{5(-12 - 32)}{9}$ — Substitute the value of F into the formula.

$C = \dfrac{5 \times (-44)}{9}$ — Work out the brackets first, then multiply by $\frac{5}{9}$

$C = -24.\dot{4}°C$ or $-24\frac{4}{9}°C$

Rearranging formulae

The **subject of a formula** is the letter that appears on its own on one side of the formula.

Examples

Make p the subject of these formulae.

a) $r = (p + 6)^2$

$r = (p + 6)^2$ — Deal with the power first. Take the square root of both sides.

$+\sqrt{r} = p + 6$ — Remove any terms added or subtracted. So subtract 6 from both sides.

$\pm\sqrt{r} - 6 = p$ **or** $p = \pm\sqrt{r} - 6$ — The subject of the formula is usually written first.

b) $y = \dfrac{p + r}{6}$

$y = \dfrac{p + r}{6}$ — First deal with the term dividing p; multiply both sides by 6.

$6y = p + r$ — Remove r by subtracting r from both sides.

$6y - r = p$ **or** $p = 6y - r$

The following example will help you to understand how to rearrange formulae when the subject appears in more than one term.

Example

Make y the subject of the formula $a = \dfrac{y + b}{y - c}$

$a = \dfrac{y + b}{y - c}$

$a(y - c) = y + b$ — Multiply both sides by $(y - c)$.

$ay - ac = y + b$ — Multiply out the brackets.

$ay - y = b + ac$ — Collect the terms involving y on one side of the equation.

$y(a - 1) = b + ac$ — Factorise.

So $y = \dfrac{b + ac}{a - 1}$

Practise plenty of questions on this topic to help you become confident when working with more complex algebra. GCSE questions on this topic usually carry a lot of marks.

Quick test

1. Using $p = 6.2$, $r = -3.2$ and $s = 3$, find the value of A in each of the following formulae.
   a) $A = pr + s$ **b)** $A = p^2s - r$ **c)** $A = r^2 - \dfrac{p}{s}$ **d)** $A = (ps - r)^2$

2. Make u the subject of the formula $v^2 = u^2 + 2as$.

3. $V = IR$. Make R the subject of the formula.

4. Make r the subject of the formula $p = \dfrac{r - y}{r + s}$

The quadratic formula

The quadratic formula

If a quadratic equation of the form $ax^2 + bx + c = 0$ cannot be solved by factorisation or completing the square (see pages 34–37), the following quadratic formula can be used:

$$x = \frac{-b \pm \sqrt{b^2 - 4ac}}{2a}$$

This formula can be used for any quadratic equation written in the form $ax^2 + bx + c = 0$.

Examples

a) Find the solutions of $2x^2 + x = 7$ to 2 decimal places.

❶ Put the equation into the form $ax^2 + bx + c = 0$.
$2x^2 + x - 7 = 0$

❷ Identify the values of a, b and c:
$a = 2$, $b = 1$, $c = -7$

❸ Substitute these values into the quadratic formula:

$$x = \frac{-b \pm \sqrt{b^2 - 4ac}}{2a}$$

$$x = \frac{-1 \pm \sqrt{1^2 - (4 \times 2 \times -7)}}{2 \times 2} = \frac{-1 \pm \sqrt{1 + 56}}{4}$$

$$= \frac{-1 \pm \sqrt{57}}{4}$$

One solution is when we use $-\sqrt{57}$: $x = \frac{-1 - \sqrt{57}}{4} = -2.14$

The other solution is when we use $+\sqrt{57}$: $x = \frac{-1 + \sqrt{57}}{4} = 1.64$

❹ To check, put these values into the original equation.

$2 \times (-2.14)^2 + (-2.14) = 7$ ✓

$2 \times (1.64)^2 + (1.64) = 7$ ✓

b) The diagram shows a trapezium. The measurements are in centimetres and the area of the trapezium is 85cm². Work out the height of the trapezium, giving your answer to 2 decimal places.

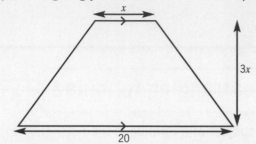

❶ The formula for the area of a trapezium is $A = \frac{1}{2}(a + b) \times h$

❷ Substituting the values above gives
$85 = \frac{1}{2} \times (x + 20) \times 3x$

❸ Multiply by 2: $170 = 3x(x + 20)$

❹ Multiply out the brackets: $170 = 3x^2 + 60x$

❺ Rearrange into the form $ax^2 + bx + c = 0$, then solve using the quadratic formula:

$3x^2 + 60x - 170 = 0 \quad a = 3, b = 60, c = -170$

$$x = \frac{-b \pm \sqrt{b^2 - 4ac}}{2a}$$

$$x = \frac{-60 \pm \sqrt{60^2 - (4 \times 3 \times -170)}}{2 \times 3}$$

$$x = \frac{-60 \pm \sqrt{5640}}{6}$$

$$x = \frac{-60 + 75.09...}{6} \text{ or } x = \frac{-60 - 75.09...}{6}$$

$x = 2.52$ or $x = -22.52$

Since length cannot be a negative, ignore the negative value of x.

❻ Height of trapezium $= 3 \times 2.52$
$= 7.56$cm

💡 *Make sure you check that you have answered the question.*

Quick test

❶ Use the quadratic formula to solve the following, giving your answers to 2 decimal places. 🖩
   a) $x^2 + 6x + 2 = 0$ **b)** $2x^2 - 6 = 7x$ **c)** $5x^2 - 5x = 18$

Algebra

Direct & inverse proportion

Direct proportion

The sign $\propto$ means 'is directly proportional to'. This is often abbreviated to 'is proportional to'. For example, $y \propto x^3$ is read as 'y is proportional to x cubed'. $y \propto x$ means that when x is multiplied by a number, then so is the corresponding value of y. For example:

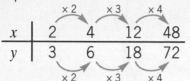

x	2	4	12	48
y	3	6	18	72

For **direct proportion**, the graph of y against x goes through the origin. For $y \propto x$, the graph is a straight line through the origin.

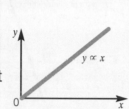

Inverse proportion

$y \propto \frac{1}{x}$ means that y is **inversely proportional** to x: when x is multiplied by a number, then y is divided by that number, and vice versa. For example:

x	4	16	48	24
y	12	3	1	2

For **inverse proportion**, the graphs of y against x go to infinity when x or $y = 0$.

The graph of $y \propto \frac{1}{x}$ looks like this:

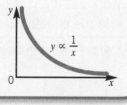

Variation

Variation questions are common on GCSE papers and they usually include statements such as...
- 'a is proportional to the square of b'
- 'c is proportional to the square root of d'
- 'p is inversely proportional to a^2'
- 'd varies as the square of x'.

Example
The value (V) of a diamond varies directly with the square of its weight (w). A diamond weighing 5.0g is worth £2500. How heavy is a diamond that is worth £6000?

❶ Change the sentence into a proportionality expression using the symbol $\propto$: $V \propto w^2$

❷ Replace $\propto$ with '$= k$' to make an equation:
$V = kw^2$

❸ Substitute the values given in the question in order to find k: $2500 = k \times 5^2$

❹ Rearrange the equation to find the value of k.
$\frac{2500}{5^2} = k \therefore k = 100$

❺ Put the value of k back into the equation:
$V = 100w^2$

❻ Now answer the question using the equation you have found.
$6000 = 100 \times w^2$
$\frac{6000}{100} = w^2$
$w = \sqrt{60} = 7.75\text{g (2 d.p.)}$

You use exactly the same steps if y is inversely proportional to x squared, except the equation in ❷ would be $y = \frac{k}{x^2}$

Quick test

❶ y is inversely proportional to the square of x. If $x = 5$ when $y = 4$, work out the value of y when $x = 10$.

❷ p varies as the square root of t. If $t = 16$ when $p = 12$, find the value of p when $t = 49$.

❸ s is inversely proportional to the cube of r. If $r = 2$ when $s = 5$, what is the value of r when $s = 10$?

Straight-line graphs

Drawing straight-line graphs

In order to draw a straight-line graph, follow these easy steps:

1. Choose three values of x and draw up a table.
2. Work out the value of y for each value of x.
3. Plot the coordinates and join up the points with a straight line.
4. Label the graph.

Example

Draw the graph of $y = 3x - 1$.

Draw up a table with some suitable values of x. Work out the y values by putting each x value into the equation.

e.g. $x = -2$ $\therefore$ $y = (3 \times -2) - 1$
$= -6 - 1 = -7$

x	-2	0	2
y	-7	-1	5

Plot the points and draw the line.

If you are asked to draw the graph $x = y + 1$, it is useful to rearrange the equation in the form $y = mx + c$ or choose coordinates of y and work out the corresponding coordinates of x.

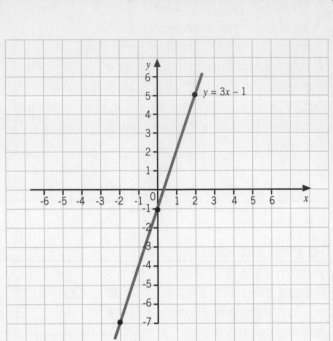

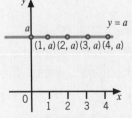 You need to be able to sketch a straight-line graph from its equation. If you can do this then you will be able to tell if the graph you have drawn is correct.

Graphs of $y = a$, $x = b$ and $x + y = k$

$y = a$ is a horizontal line with every y coordinate equal to a.

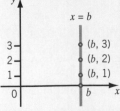

$x = b$ is a vertical line with every x coordinate equal to b.

Graphs of $x + y = k$, where k is a number, always give straight-line graphs. Tables of values are not needed when drawing this type of graph.

Example

Draw the graph of $x + y = 3$.

On the x-axis, $y = 0$, so $x = 3$ since $3 + 0 = 3$. On the y-axis, $x = 0$, so $y = 3$ since $0 + 3 = 3$. The graph goes straight through the points (3, 0) and (0, 3).

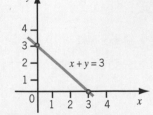

Algebra

Interpreting $y = mx + c$

The general equation of a straight-line graph is
$y = mx + c$
where m is the **gradient** (steepness) of the line.

Remember these points about straight-line graphs:
- As m increases, the line gets steeper.
- If m is positive, the line slopes forwards.
- If m is negative, the line slopes backwards.
- c is the **intercept** on the y-axis, that is, where the graph cuts the y-axis.
- **Parallel** lines have the same gradient.
- If two lines are **perpendicular**, the product of their gradients is -1.

If a line has a gradient of m, then a line that is perpendicular to it will have a gradient of $\frac{-1}{m}$. In the diagram top right, the lines $y = -2x$ and $y = \frac{1}{2}x$ are perpendicular because $-2 \times \frac{1}{2} = -1$.

Example
Write down the equation of a line that is perpendicular to $y = 5 - 3x$ and that goes through the point (0, 2).

1. Rewrite the equation in the form $y = mx + c$, so $y = -3x + 5$.
2. Since perpendicular gradients multiply to give -1:
   $-3 \times \frac{1}{3} = -1$, so $y = \frac{1}{3}x + c$
   Line goes through (0, 2), hence $c = 2$.
3. Equation of straight line is $y = \frac{1}{3}x + 2$.

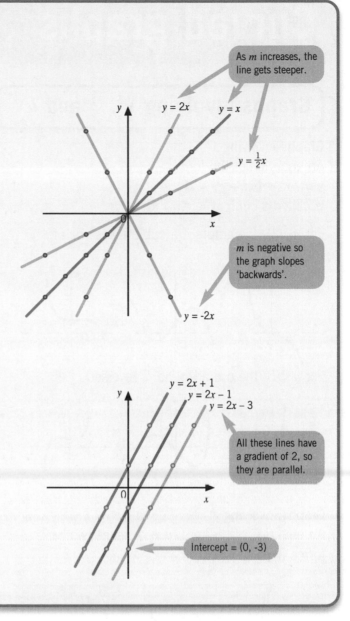

As m increases, the line gets steeper.

$y = 2x$ $y = x$

$y = \frac{1}{2}x$

m is negative so the graph slopes 'backwards'.

$y = -2x$

$y = 2x + 1$
$y = 2x - 1$
$y = 2x - 3$

All these lines have a gradient of 2, so they are parallel.

Intercept = (0, -3)

Finding the gradient of a line

To find the **gradient** of a line, follow these steps:
1. Choose two points on the line.
2. Draw a triangle as shown.
3. Find the change in y (height) and the change in x (base).
4. Gradient = $\dfrac{\text{change in } y}{\text{change in } x}$ or $\dfrac{\text{height}}{\text{base}} = \dfrac{4}{3} = 1\frac{1}{3}$
5. Decide if the gradient is positive or negative.

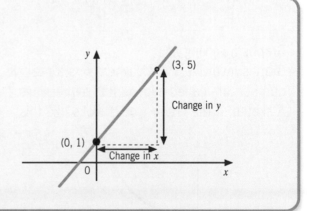

(3, 5)

Change in y

(0, 1)

Change in x

Quick test

1. Draw the graph of $y = 6 - 2x$. From your graph, write down the solution of the following equations.
   a) $6 - 2x = 4$ b) $6 - 2x = 3$

2. Write down the gradient and y-axis intercept for each of these straight-line graphs.
   a) $y = 4 + 2x$ b) $y = 3x - 2$ c) $2y = 6x + 4$

Curved graphs

Graphs involving x^3, $\frac{1}{x}$ and k^x

Graphs involving x^3
An equation of the form
$$y = ax^3 + bx^2 + cx + d$$
is called a **cubic** where $a \neq 0$.

For $a > 0$, the graph of a cubic takes one of these forms:

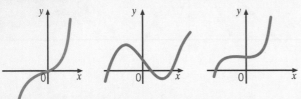

For $a < 0$, the overall trend is reversed:

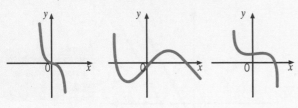

Graphs involving $\frac{1}{x}$
An equation of the form $y = \frac{a}{x}$ takes two basic forms depending on the value of a.

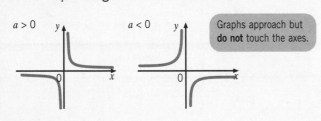

Graphs approach but **do not** touch the axes.

Graphs involving k^x
Graphs involving $y = k^x$, where k is a positive number, are called **exponential expressions**. A sketch of the graph $y = 2^x$ looks like this:

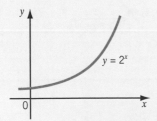

The graph $y = 2^x$ has no maximum or minimum point. It crosses the y-axis at the point (0, 1). The value of y increases rapidly as the value of x increases. When x is negative, the value of y approaches zero. The graph never crosses the x-axis.

Example
Draw the graph of $y = x^2 + 4 + \frac{2}{x}$ for $-3 \leqslant x \leqslant 3$.

❶ Make a table of values:

x	x^2	4	$+\frac{2}{x}$	y
-3	9	4	-0.$\dot{6}$	12.$\dot{3}$
-2	4	4	-1	7
-1	1	4	-2	3
-0.5	0.25	4	-4	0.25
-0.2	0.04	4	-10	-5.96
There is no 0 row since you cannot calculate $\frac{2}{x}$ if $x = 0$.				
0.2	0.04	4	10	14.04
0.5	0.25	4	4	8.25
1	1	4	2	7
2	4	4	1	9
3	9	4	0.$\dot{6}$	13.$\dot{6}$

❷ Plot the points and draw a smooth curve (see graph $y = x^2 + 4 + \frac{2}{x}$ below).

There will be a break in the curve at $x = 0$.

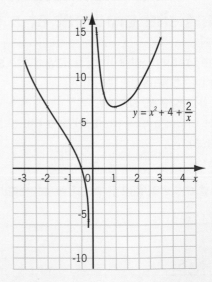

Algebra

48

Graphs of the form $y = ax^2 + bx + c$

Graphs of the form $y = ax^2 + bx + c$ are called **quadratic graphs** where $a \neq 0$. These graphs are curved and are known as **parabolas**.

If $a > 0$, the graph is U-shaped.

If $a < 0$, the graph has an upside-down U.

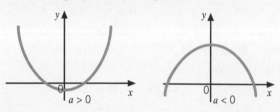

Example

Draw the graph of $y = x^2 - x - 6$ using values of x from -2 to 3. Use the graph to find the value of x when $y = -3$.

When drawing a quadratic graph follow these steps:

❶ Make a table of values. Work out the values of y by substituting the values of x into the equation:

e.g. If $x = 1$ $y = x^2 - x - 6$

$= 1^2 - 1 - 6 = -6$

x	-2	-1	0	1	2	3	0.5
y	0	-4	-6	-6	-4	0	-6.25

$x = 0.5$ is worked out to find the minimum value.

❷ Plot the points and join them with a smooth curve.

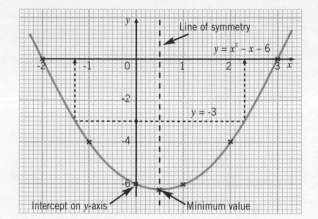

💡 *Draw the curve with a sharp pencil, go through all the points and check for any parts that look wrong.*

The graph shows the following:

- The **minimum value** is when $x = 0.5$, $y = -6.25$
- The **line of symmetry** is at $x = 0.5$
- The curve cuts the y-axis at $(0, -6)$, i.e. $(0, c)$
- When $y = -3$, read across from $y = -3$ to the graph, then read up to the x-axis:

$x = 2.3$ and $x = -1.3$

These are the approximate solutions of the equation $x^2 - x - 6 = -3$.

Quick test

❶ a) Complete the table of values for the graph $y = x^3 + 3$. 🖩

x	-3	-2	-1	0	1	2	3
y							

b) Draw the graph of $y = x^3 + 3$. Use scales of 1 unit per 2cm on the x-axis and 10 units per 2cm on the y-axis.

c) From your graph, find the value of x when $y = 15$.

❷ Match each of the four graphs below with one of the following equations.

- $y = 2x - 5$
- $y = x^2 + 3$
- $y = 3 - x^2$
- $y = 5 - x$
- $y = x^3$
- $y = \dfrac{2}{x}$

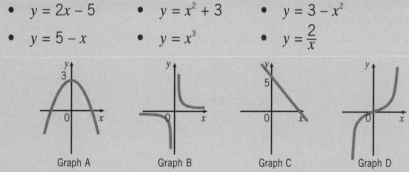

Graph A   Graph B   Graph C   Graph D

Advanced graphs

Solving quadratic and linear equations simultaneously

We have already seen that the point where two graphs meet represents the simultaneous solutions of the equations. So far we have only looked at linear equations and their corresponding straight-line graphs. You also need to be able to work out the coordinates of the points of intersection of a straight line and a quadratic curve.

The diagram shows the points of intersection of the straight line $y = 5x - 6$ and the curve $y = x^2$.

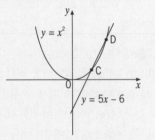

To find the coordinates of the points of intersection, C and D, of the line $y = 5x - 6$ and the curve $y = x^2$, we know that the points C and D both lie on the curve and the line, giving us the simultaneous equations:

$y = 5x - 6$ ① $y = x^2$ ②

❶ Eliminate y by substituting equation ② into equation ① (or by subtracting equation ① from equation ②): $x^2 = 5x - 6$

❷ Rearrange: $x^2 - 5x + 6 = 0$

❸ Factorise; $(x - 2)(x - 3) = 0$
and solve: $x = 2$ and $x = 3$

These are the x coordinates of the points of intersection.

❹ Substitute the values of x back into equation ① to find the y coordinates:

$x = 2$: $y = 5x - 6$
          $y = 5 \times 2 - 6$
          $y = 4$ Coordinate of C (2, 4)

$x = 3$: $y = 5x - 6$
          $y = 5 \times 3 - 6$
          $y = 9$ Coordinate of D (3, 9)

So the line $y = 5x - 6$ intersects the curve $y = x^2$ at (2, 4) and (3, 9).

Remember, solving a quadratic and linear equation gives the point of intersection of the two graphs.

The intersection of a circle and a line

The equation of a circle can be found by using Pythagoras' theorem. The equation of any circle with centre (0, 0) and radius r is $x^2 + y^2 = r^2$

Example

Find the coordinates of the points where the line $y - 5 = x$ cuts the circle $x^2 + y^2 = 25$.

❶ The coordinates of the points of intersection must lie on the circle and the line. The coordinates must satisfy both equations:

$y - 5 = x$ ① $x^2 + y^2 = 25$ ②

❷ Rewrite equation ① in the form '$y = ...$'

$y = x + 5$ ①

❸ Eliminate y by substituting ① into ②.
Expand brackets: $x^2 + (x + 5)^2 = 25$
          $x^2 + x^2 + 10x + 25 = 25$
Rearrange: $2x^2 + 10x = 0$
Factorise: $2x(x + 5) = 0$
          So $x = 0$ or $x = -5$

❹ Substitute the values of x into equation ① to find the values of y:

$x = 0$: $y = 0 + 5 = 5$
$x = -5$: $y = -5 + 5 = 0$

The line $y = x + 5$ cuts the circle $x^2 + y^2 = 25$ at (0, 5) and (-5, 0).

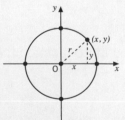

Functions and transformations

If y = 'an expression involving x' then it can be written as $y = f(x)$.

The graphs of related functions can be found by applying the following **transformations**:

- $y = f(x) \pm a$ moves the graphs up or down the y-axis by a value of a, i.e. a translation of $\begin{pmatrix} 0 \\ \pm a \end{pmatrix}$.

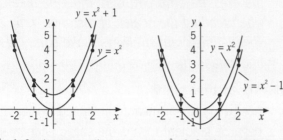

$y = x^2 + 1$: Graph moves up the y-axis by one unit.

$y = x^2 - 1$: Graph moves down the y-axis by one unit.

- $y = f(x \pm a)$ moves the whole graph a units to the left or right. They move in the opposite direction to what you would think!

  $y = f(x + a)$ moves the graph a units to the left, i.e. a translation of $\begin{pmatrix} -a \\ 0 \end{pmatrix}$.

  $y = f(x - a)$ moves the graph a units to the right, i.e. a translation of $\begin{pmatrix} a \\ 0 \end{pmatrix}$.

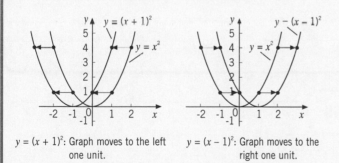

$y = (x + 1)^2$: Graph moves to the left one unit.

$y = (x - 1)^2$: Graph moves to the right one unit.

The four graph transformations need to be learned – they often appear on the exam paper.

- $y = a \times f(x)$ stretches the original graph along the y-axis by a factor of a.
  If $a > 1$, e.g. $y = 2x^2$, all the points are stretched upwards in the y direction by a scale factor of 2.
  If $a < 1$, e.g. $y = \frac{1}{2}x^2$, the graph is squashed downwards by a scale factor of $\frac{1}{2}$

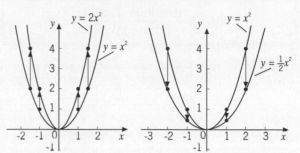

The x values stay the same and the y values are multiplied by 2.

The x values stay the same and the y values are multiplied by $\frac{1}{2}$.

- $y = f(ax)$ This is sometimes confusing. If $a > 1$, the graph stretches inwards in the x direction by $\frac{1}{a}$, e.g., if $y = (2x)^2$, the x coordinates are multiplied by $\frac{1}{2}$
  If $a < 1$, the graph stretches outwards in the x direction by $\frac{1}{a}$, e.g., if $y = (\frac{1}{2}x)^2$, the x coordinates are multiplied by 2 $(1 \div \frac{1}{2} = 2)$.

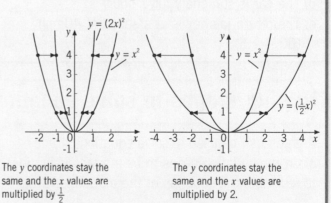

The y coordinates stay the same and the x values are multiplied by $\frac{1}{2}$.

The y coordinates stay the same and the x values are multiplied by 2.

Quick test

1. Sketch the following graphs.
   a) $y = x^3$ b) $y = x^3 - 4$
   c) $y = (x - 2)^3$ d) $y = 2x^3$

2. Solve the simultaneous equations $y = x^2$ and $y = 3x + 4$.

Interpreting graphs

Distance–time graphs and speed–time graphs

Distance–time graphs are often called **travel graphs**. The **speed** of an object can be found from the gradient of the line.

$$\text{Speed} = \frac{\text{distance travelled}}{\text{time taken}}$$

Example

The graph shows Mr Rogers' car journey. He set off at 9am (0900). Work out the speed of each stage.

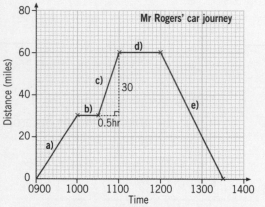

a) The car is travelling at 30mph for 1 hour (30 ÷ 1).

b) The car is stationary for 30 minutes.

c) The graph is steeper so the car is travelling faster, at a speed of 60mph for 30 minutes (30 ÷ 0.5).

d) The car is stationary for 1 hour.

e) The return journey is at a speed of 40mph (60 ÷ 1.5).

> Notice the importance of using the gradient of a line. It is useful to note that on the distance–time graph example, the scales on the axes are different. Care must be taken when reading the scales of distance–time and speed–time graphs: always make sure you understand the scales before you start.

In a speed–time graph…
- a positive gradient means the speed is increasing
- a negative gradient means the speed is decreasing
- a horizontal line means the speed is constant
- distance travelled is the area between the graph and the x-axis.

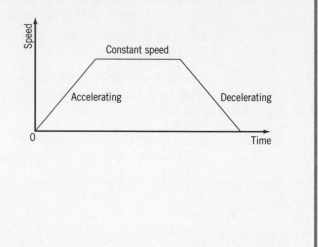

Using graphs to solve equations

A graph can be used to solve equations. Quite often the equation needs to be rearranged in order to resemble the equation of the plotted graph.

Example

The graph $y = x^2 - 2x + 1$ is drawn opposite. Use the graph to solve the following equations.

a) $x^2 - 2x + 1 = 6$

Our graph is $y = x^2 - 2x + 1$. The solutions are where the line $y = 6$ crosses the graph:
$x = -1.45$, and $x = 3.45$

b) $x^2 - 3x = 0$

We need to rearrange the equation so it is like our graph:

$x^2 - 3x = 0$

$x^2 - 3x + x + 1 = x + 1$ ⬜ Add $x + 1$ to both sides.

$x^2 - 2x + 1 = x + 1$

Our graph is $y = x^2 - 2x + 1$. The solutions are where the graph crosses the line $y = x + 1$:
$x = 0$ and $x = 3$.

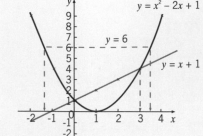

Algebra

Using graphs to find relationships

Sometimes you will be given a table of data that is known to fit a relationship. If a suitable graph is drawn, the relationship can be found.

Example

The graph below is known to fit the relationship $y = pq^x$ where p and q are positive constants. Use the graph to find the values of p and q and the relationship.

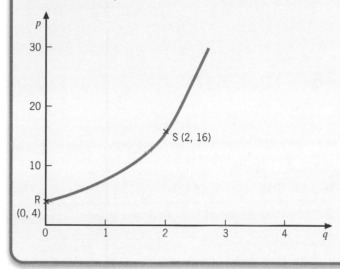

In order to find values for p and q, we need to take values at R and S, then substitute them into the equation $y = pq^x$.

At point R, $x = 0$ and $y = 4$

So $y = pq^x$ becomes

$4 = p \times q^0$ Remember, $q^0 = 1$.

$4 = p$

At point S, $x = 2$ and $y = 16$

So $16 = 4 \times q^2$

$16 \div 4 = q^2$ Divide both sides by 4.

$4 = q^2$

$q = \sqrt{4} = 2$

The relationship is $y = 4 \times 2^x$.

To find different coordinates on the graph, the $\boxed{x^y}$ button on the calculator is used.

When $x = 7$, $y = 4 \times 2^7 = 512$

N.B. You also need to revise work on **conversion graphs.**

Quick test

1

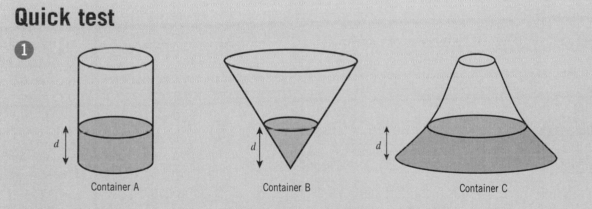

Container A   Container B   Container C

These containers are being filled with a liquid at a rate of 150ml per second. The graphs show how the depth of the water (d) changes with time (t). Match the containers with the graphs below.

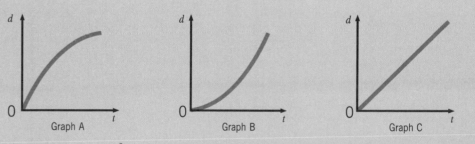

Graph A   Graph B   Graph C

2 Draw the graph of $y = x^2 + x - 2$. Use your graph to solve the following equations. 📟

a) $x^2 + x = 5$

b) $x^2 - 2 = 0$

c) $x^2 - 2x - 2 = 0$

Practice questions

Use these questions to test your progress. Check your answers on page 111. You may wish to answer these questions on a separate piece of paper so that you can show full working out, which you will be expected to do in the exam.

1 Solve the following equations.
   a) $2x + 4 = 10$ **b)** $3x - 1 = 11$ **c)** $5x - 3 = 2x + 12$
   d) $3(x + 1) = 9$ **e)** $2(x + 1) = x + 3$

2 **a)** Here are the first five terms of a number sequence: 7, 12, 17, 22, 27, ...
   Write down an expression for the nth term of the sequence.

   b) Here are the first five terms of a different sequence: 5, 14, 29, 50, 77, ...
   Write down an expression for the nth term of the sequence.

3 Simplify...
   a) $3x^2 \times 4x^2$ **b)** $6x^2y \times 2x^3y^2$ **c)** $12y^4 \div 3y$ **d)** $(3y^2)^2$

4 Solve the simultaneous equations: $4a + 3b = 6$ $2a - 3b = 12$

5 $p^2 = 5xy - 3x^2$

   a) Calculate the positive value of p when $x = 5.8$ and $y = 105$.

   b) Rearrange the formula $p^2 = 5xy - 3x^2$ to make y the subject.

6 The equation $x^3 - 2x = 2$ has a solution between 1 and 2. By using a method of trial and improvement, find this solution to 1 decimal place.

7 Solve the inequality $2 \leqslant 5n - 3 \leqslant 12$.

8 Match the graphs with the equations.
   a) $y = x^2 - 4$ **b)** $y = 2x + 1$ **c)** $y = 3 - 4x$ **d)** $xy = 6$

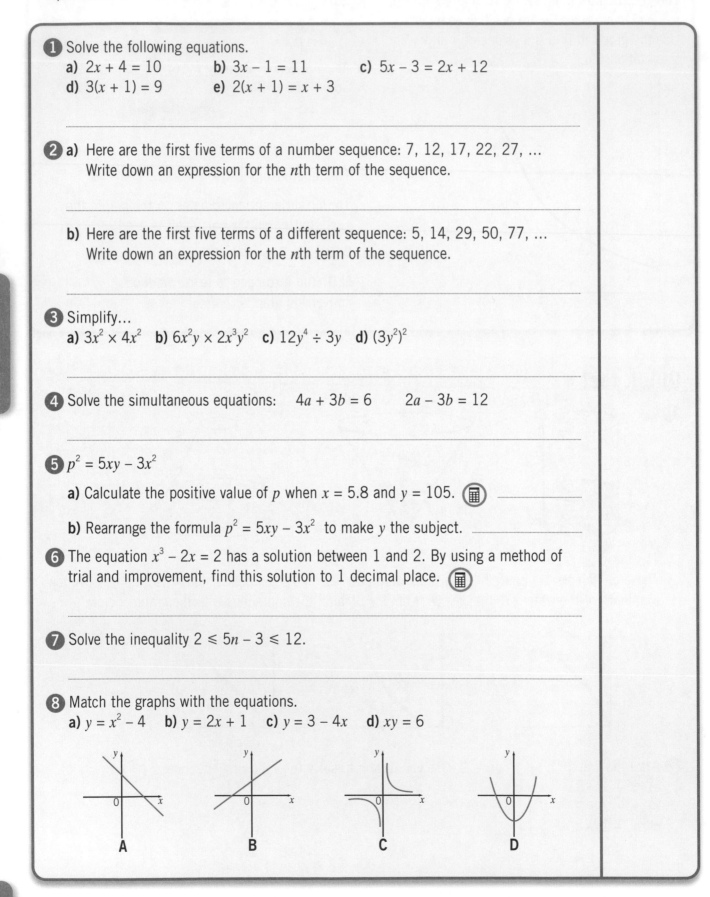

A   B   C   D

Algebra

9 Simplify... **a)** $\dfrac{2}{(x+4)} + \dfrac{3}{(x-2)}$ **b)** $\dfrac{6}{x-3} - \dfrac{2}{x+4}$ **c)** $\dfrac{4a^2b}{a^4b} \times \dfrac{a^3b^2}{8ab^2}$

10 Simplify $\dfrac{x^2 - 16}{2x^2 - 11x + 12}$

11 Solve these equations by using the quadratic formula. Give your answers to 3 s.f. 📱
   a) $3x^2 - 4x - 2 = 0$ **b)** $5x^2 - 3x - 1 = 0$

12 If the area of the rectangle is 50cm²...
   a) show that $x^2 + x - 27 = 0$

   (2x + 4)cm
   (x – 1)cm   Area = 50cm²

   b) work out the length of the rectangle. 📱

13 Solve the simultaneous equations and interpret your solution geometrically. 📱
   $x^2 + y^2 = 16$ and $y = x + 4$

14 Make p the subject of the formula $6p + 2r = x(4 - p)$.

15 This is the graph of $y = f(x)$. On a separate
   piece of paper, draw a sketch of...
   a) $y = f(x + 2)$
   b) $y = f(x) - 3$
   c) $y = -f(x)$
   d) $y = f(2x)$

   y = f(x)

16 Amy, Beth and Cara are three friends. Amy has £2y. Beth has £1 more than Amy.
   Amy gives one third of her money to Cara and keeps the rest. Beth gives one fifth of
   her money to Cara and keeps the rest. Cara is given a total of £5.
   a) Show that $\dfrac{2y}{3} + \dfrac{2y + 1}{5} = 5$

   b) Find out how much money Beth keeps.

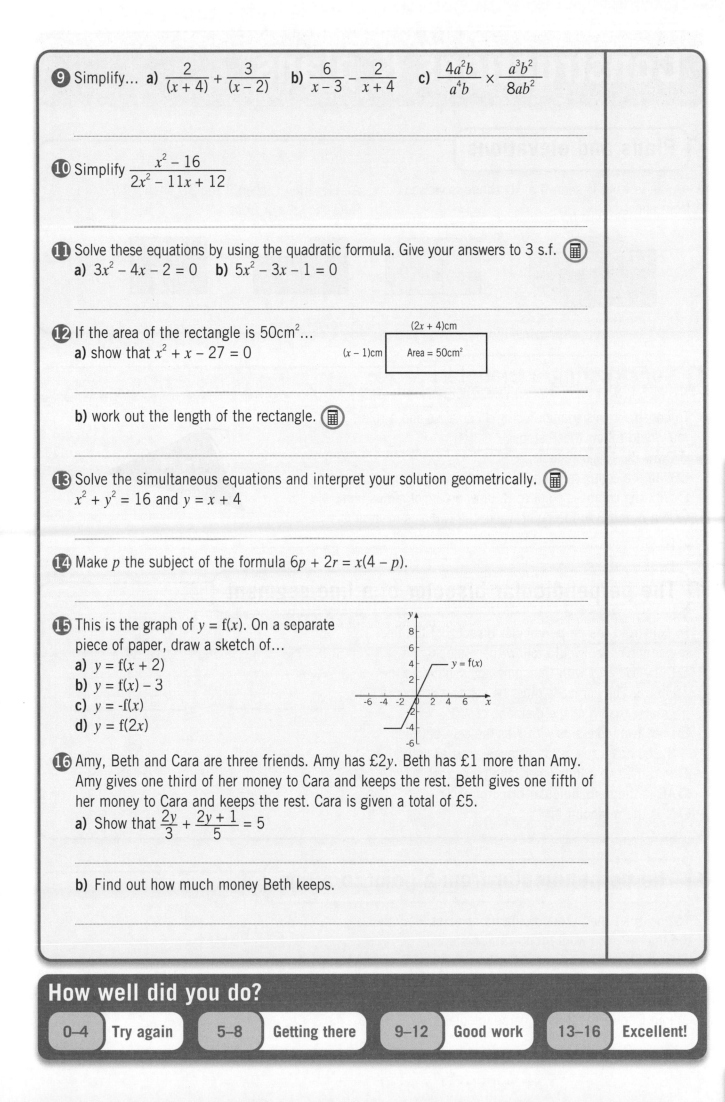

How well did you do?

| 0–4 | Try again | 5–8 | Getting there | 9–12 | Good work | 13–16 | Excellent! |

Constructions & plans

Plans and elevations

A **plan** is what is seen if a 3D shape is viewed from above.

An **elevation** is seen if the 3D shape is viewed from the side or front.

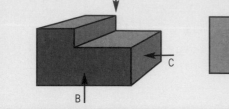

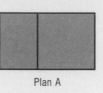

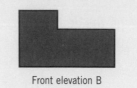

Plan A

Front elevation B

Side elevation C

Constructing a triangle

To construct this triangle using a compass and a ruler, you would follow these steps:

❶ Draw the longest side.
❷ With the compass point at A, draw an arc of radius 4cm.
❸ With the compass point at B, draw an arc of radius 5cm.
❹ Join A and B to the point where the two arcs meet at C.

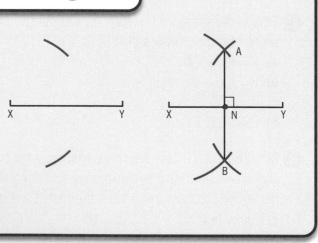

Not to scale

The perpendicular bisector of a line segment

To construct the **perpendicular bisector** of the **line segment** XY, you would follow these steps:

❶ Draw two arcs with the compass, using X as the centre. The compass must be set at a radius greater than half the distance of XY.
❷ Draw two more arcs with Y as the centre. (Keep the compass the same distance apart as before.)
❸ Join the two points where the arcs cross.
❹ AB is the **perpendicular bisector** of XY.
❺ N is the **midpoint** of XY.

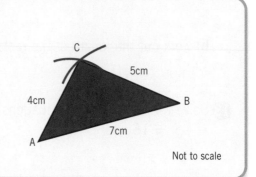

The perpendicular from a point to a line

To construct the perpendicular from point P to the line AB, you would follow these steps:

❶ From P, draw arcs to cut the line at A and B.
❷ From A and B, draw arcs with the same radius to intersect at a point C below the line.
❸ Join P to C; this line is perpendicular to AB.

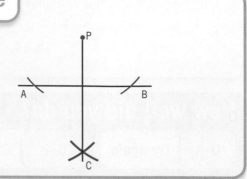

The perpendicular from a point on a straight line

To construct the perpendicular at the point N on a straight line, you would follow these steps:

❶ With the compass set to a radius of several centimetres, and centred on N, draw arcs to cut the line at A and B.

❷ Construct the **perpendicular bisector** of the line segment AB as on page 56.

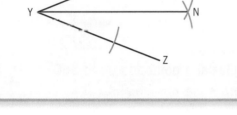

Bisecting an angle

To bisect an angle, follow these steps:

❶ Draw two lines, XY and YZ, to meet at an angle.

❷ Using a compass, place the point at Y and draw the two arcs on XY and YZ.

❸ Place the compass point at the two arcs on XY and YZ and draw arcs to cross at N.

❹ Join Y and N. YN is the **bisector** of angle XYZ.

Construction of an inscribed regular polygon

Example

Construct a regular hexagon inside a circle of radius 2cm.

Draw a circle of radius 2cm and mark a point P on its circumference.

Keeping the compass set at 2cm, draw an arc, centre P, which cuts the circle at Q. Q is the centre of the next arc.

Repeat the process until six points are marked on the circumference. Join the points to make a hexagon.

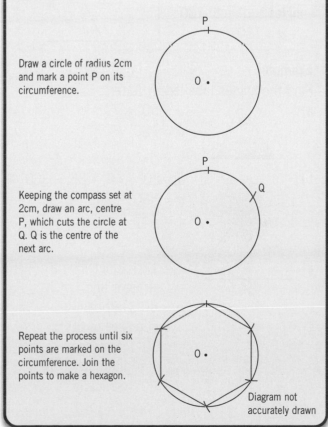

Diagram not accurately drawn

Constructing an angle of 60°

Example

Construct an angle of 60° at point P on a line segment AB.

❶ Place the compass point on P and draw an arc that starts just below the line AB and ends almost above P.

❷ Label point C where the arc intersects AB.

❸ Keeping the radius the same, from point C draw an arc to intersect the first arc at D. Angle DPC is 60°.

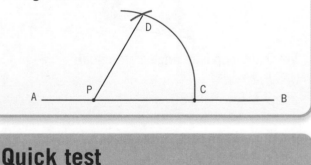

Quick test

❶ Bisect this angle.

❷ Draw the perpendicular bisector of a 10cm line.

Diagram drawn to scale

Angles

Types of angles

An **acute angle** is between 0° and 90°.

An **obtuse angle** is between 90° and 180°.

A **reflex angle** is between 180° and 360°.

A **right angle** is 90°.

Angle facts

Angles on a straight line add up to **180°**.
$a + b + c = 180°$

Angles at a point add up to **360°**.
$a + b + c + d = 360°$

Angles in a triangle add up to **180°**.
$a + b + c = 180°$

Angles in a quadrilateral add up to **360°**.
$a + b + c + d = 360°$

Vertically-opposite angles are **equal**.
$a = b, c = d$
$a + d = b + c = 180°$

An **exterior angle** of a triangle equals the sum of the **two opposite interior angles**. $a + b = c$

Reading angles

When asked to find angle XYZ or ∠XYZ or XŶZ, find the **middle letter angle**, angle Y.

Angles in parallel lines

Alternate angles are **equal**.	
Corresponding angles are **equal**.	
Supplementary (allied) angles add up to **180°**: $c + d = 180°$	

Examples

Find the angles labelled by letters.

a) $a = 50° + 70°$
             $a = 120°$

b) $a + 80° + 40° + 85° = 360°$
             $a = 360° - 205°$
             $a = 155°$

c) $a = 120°$ (angles on a straight line)
             $b = 60°$ (vertically opposite to 60°)
             $c = 60°$ (corresponding to b or alternate to 60°)
             $d = 60°$ (vertically opposite to c)

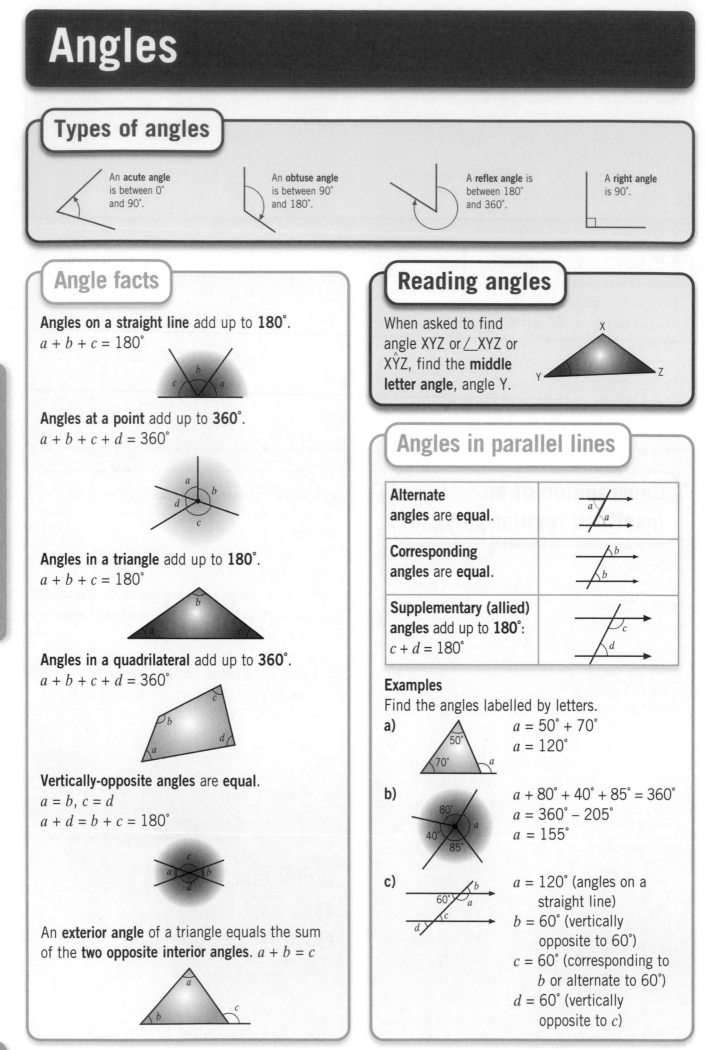

Polygons

Polygons are 2D shapes with straight sides.
Regular polygons are shapes with all sides and angles equal.

Number of sides	Name of polygon
3	Triangle
4	Quadrilateral
5	Pentagon
6	Hexagon
7	Heptagon
8	Octagon
9	Nonagon
10	Decagon

Remember to learn the properties of quadrilaterals.

Tessellations

A tessellation is a pattern of 2D shapes that fit together without leaving any gaps.

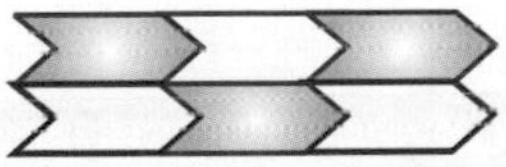

For shapes to tessellate, the angles at each point must add up to 360°.

For example, regular pentagons will not tessellate. Each interior angle is 108°, and 3 × 108° = 324°.

A gap of 360° − 324° = 36° is left.

M.C. Escher is a famous artist who used tessellations in his art work. Tessellations are often seen in mosaics and floor tiles.

Angles in a polygon

There are two types of angle in any polygon: interior (inside) and exterior (outside).

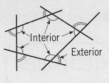

For a polygon with n sides...

- sum of exterior angles = 360°. For a regular polygon with n sides, exterior angle = $\dfrac{360°}{n}$

- interior angle + exterior angle = 180°

- sum of interior angles = $(n - 2) \times 180°$ or $(2n - 4) \times 90°$

Examples

a) A regular polygon has an interior angle of 150°. How many sides does it have?

Let n be the number of sides.
Exterior + interior = 180°
Exterior angle = 180° − 150° = 30°
Exterior angle = $\dfrac{360°}{n}$

So $n = \dfrac{360°}{\text{exterior angle}} = \dfrac{360°}{30°} = 12$

The polygon has 12 sides. (It is a dodecagon.)

b) The diagram shows an irregular pentagon. Work out the size of x.

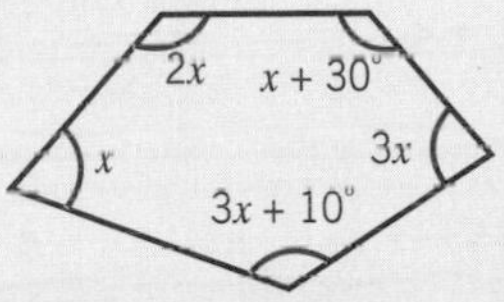

Sum of interior angles:
$(5 - 2) \times 180°$
$= 3 \times 180° = 540°$

Form an equation and solve it to find x:
$x + 2x + x + 30° + 3x + 3x + 10° = 540°$
$10x + 40° = 540°$
$\qquad 10x = 540° - 40°$
$\qquad 10x = 500°$
$\qquad\quad x = 50°$

Make sure that you show full working out when carrying out an angle calculation. If you are asked to 'Explain', always refer to the angle properties, e.g. angles on a straight line add up to 180°.

Quick test

1 Find the sizes of the angles labelled by letters.

a)   b)   c)

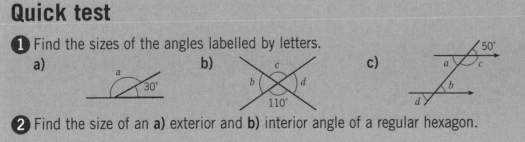

2 Find the size of an a) exterior and b) interior angle of a regular hexagon.

Bearings & scale drawings

Bearings

A **bearing** is the direction travelled between two points, given as an angle in degrees:
- All bearings are measured **clockwise from the north** line.
- All bearings should be given as three figures, e.g. 225°, 043°, 006°.

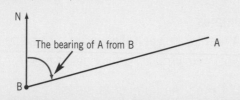

The bearing of A from B

Back bearings

To find the **back bearing** (the bearing of Q from P in the examples below):

❶ Draw in a north line at P.

❷ The two north lines are parallel lines, so the angle properties of parallel lines can be used.

💡 *The word 'from' is important when answering bearing questions. It tells you where to put the north line and where to measure.*

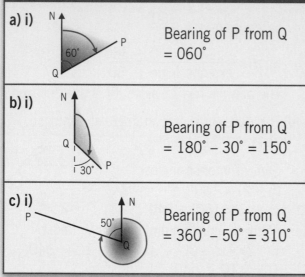

Bearings (measure from the north line at Q)

a) i) Bearing of P from Q = 060°

b) i) Bearing of P from Q = 180° − 30° = 150°

c) i) Bearing of P from Q = 360° − 50° = 310°

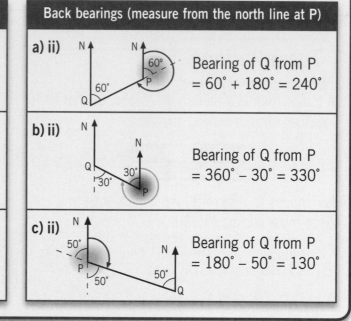

Back bearings (measure from the north line at P)

a) ii) Bearing of Q from P = 60° + 180° = 240°

b) ii) Bearing of Q from P = 360° − 30° = 330°

c) ii) Bearing of Q from P = 180° − 50° = 130°

Scale drawings and bearings

Scale drawings are useful for finding lengths and angles. They are often used by architects and surveyors.

Example

A ship sails from a harbour for 15km on a bearing of 040°, then continues due east for 20km. Make a scale drawing of this journey using a scale of 1cm to 5km. How far will the ship have to sail to get back to the harbour by the shortest route? What will the bearing be?

Shortest route = 6.4 × 5km = 32km
Bearing back to harbour = 70° + 180° = 250°

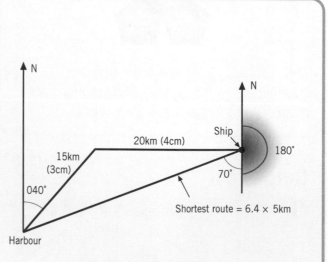

Note – this diagram is not drawn accurately but shows you what your diagram should look like.

Scales and maps

Scales are often used on maps. They are usually written as a ratio. You will use map work in geography. Orienteers use maps and compasses to find directions.

Example

The scale on a road map is 1 : 25 000. Bury and Oldham are 60cm apart on the map. Work out the real distance, in km, between Bury and Oldham.

❶ Scale 1 : 25 000, distance on map is 60cm.
   ∴ real distance = 60 × 25 000 = 1 500 000cm

❷ Divide by 100 to change cm to m:
   1 500 000 ÷ 100 = 15 000m

❸ Divide by 1000 to change m to km:
   15 000 ÷ 1000 = 15km

⚠️ *A scale of 1 : 25 000 means that 1cm on the scale drawing represents a real length of 25 000cm.*

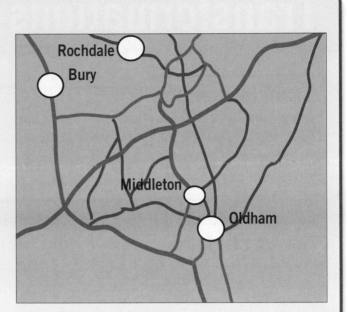

Quick test

❶ What are the bearings of A from B in the following diagrams?

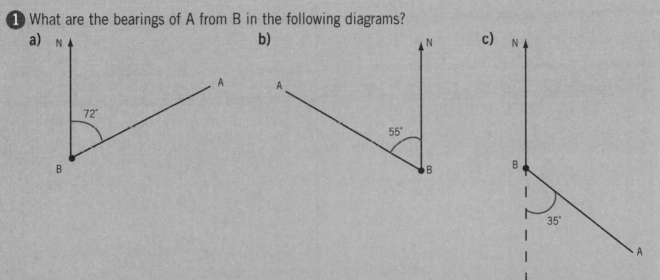

a) 72°

b) 55°

c) 35°

❷ For each of the questions above, work out the bearing of B from A.

❸ The scale on a road map is 1 : 50 000. If two towns are 14cm apart on the map, work out the real distance between them in kilometres. 🖩

Transformations 1

Transformations

A transformation changes the position or size of a shape. There are four types of transformations: translations, reflections, rotations and enlargements.

Transformations are often used in the creation of repeating wallpaper patterns.

Translations

A translation moves a figure from one place to another. The size and shape of the figure are not changed. **Vectors** are used to describe the distance and direction of a translation.

A vector is written $\binom{a}{b}$, where a represents the **horizontal** movement, and b represents the **vertical** movement.

Example
a) Translate ABC by the vector $\binom{2}{1}$. Call the image P.

> This means 2 to the right and 1 upwards.

b) Translate ABC by the vector $\binom{-3}{-2}$. Call the image Q.

> This means 3 to the left and 2 down.

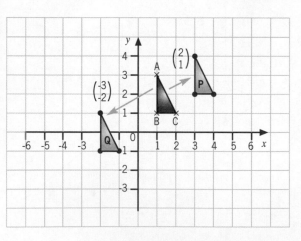

Triangles P and Q are **congruent** to triangle ABC – two or more shapes are congruent if they have exactly the same size and shape.

Reflections

A reflection creates an image of an object on the other side of the **mirror line**. The mirror line is known as an **axis of reflection**. The size and shape of the figure are not changed.

Example
Reflect triangle ABC in...
a) the x-axis, and call the image D
b) the line $y = -x$, and call the image E
c) the line $x = 5$, and call the image F.

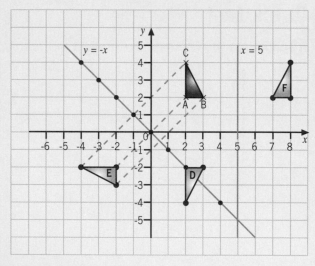

Triangles D, E and F are congruent to triangle ABC.

When describing reflections, make sure you write down the equation of the mirror line.

> Count the squares to find the perpendicular distance from the object to the mirror line. The image will be the same distance away.

Rotations

A rotation turns a figure through an angle about some fixed point. This fixed point is called the **centre of rotation**. The size and shape of the figure are not changed.

Example

Rotate triangle ABC...

a) 90° clockwise about (0, 0), and call it R

b) 180° about (0, 0), and call it S

c) 90° anticlockwise about (-1, 1), and call it T.

d) Describe the rotation that takes triangle R onto triangle V.

The rotation is 180° clockwise (or anticlockwise) about (4, -3).

> *When describing a rotation give...*
> - *the centre of rotation*
> - *the direction of the turn (clockwise or anticlockwise)*
> - *the angle of the turn.*
>
> *If you don't give all three pieces of information, you will lose marks for not describing the rotation fully.*

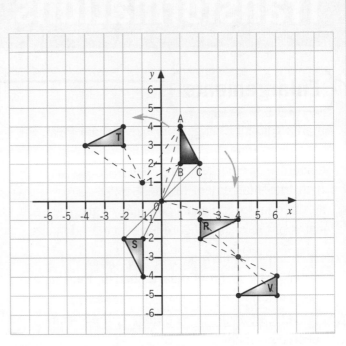

On the grid above, R, S, T and V are all congruent to triangle ABC.

Quick test

1 On the diagram opposite...

    a) translate triangle ABC by the vector $\binom{-3}{1}$ and call it P

    b) reflect ABC in the line $y = x$ and call it Q

    c) reflect ABC in the line $y = -1$ and call it R

    d) rotate ABC 180° about (0, 0) and call it S.

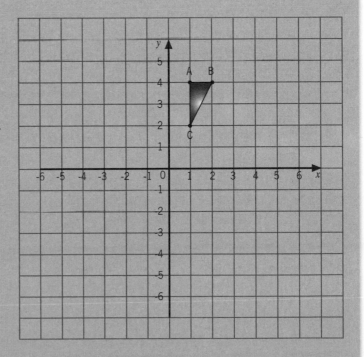

2 What does the vector $\binom{-2}{3}$ mean?

3 A point D (3, -6) moves to the point E (-2, 5). What is the vector translation that moves point D to point E?

Transformations 2

Enlargements

An enlargement changes the size but not the shape of an object.

The centre of enlargement is the point from which the enlargement takes place.

The scale factor indicates how many times the lengths of the original figure have increased in size.

Remember the following:

- If the scale factor is greater than 1, the shape becomes bigger.
- If the scale factor is less than 1, the shape becomes smaller.
- When one shape is an enlargement of another, they are similar, i.e. they are the same shape with the same angles, but different sizes.

Examples

a) Enlarge triangle ABC by a scale factor of 2, centre = (0, 0). Call it A'B'C'.

Notice each side of the enlargement is twice the length of the original.
e.g. A'B' = 2AB

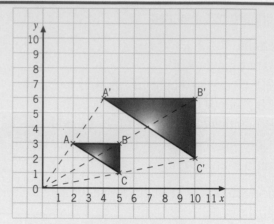

b) Describe fully the transformation that maps ABCDEF onto A'B'C'D'E'F'.

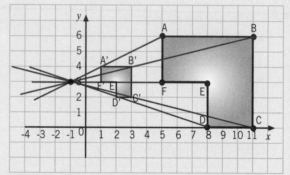

- To find the centre of enlargement, join A to A', and continue the line. Join B to B', and continue the line. Do the same for the others.
- Where all the lines meet is the centre of enlargement: (-1, 3).
- The transformation is an enlargement with scale factor $\frac{1}{3}$ and centre of enlargement at (-1, 3).

Enlargement with a negative scale factor

If the scale factor of an enlargement is negative, then the image is drawn on the opposite side of the centre of enlargement to the object. The image will also be upside down.

For example, the triangle ABC has been mapped onto $A_1B_1C_1$ by a scale factor of -2, centre at 0.

When asked to describe an enlargement, you must include both the scale factor and the position of the centre of enlargement.

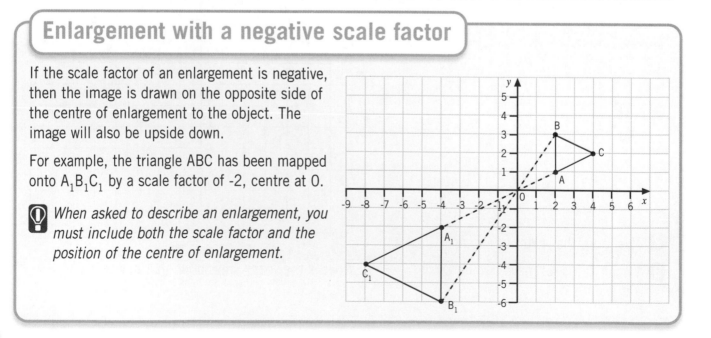

Geometry and measures

Combining transformations

Combined transformations are a series of two or more transformations.

Example

a) Reflect triangle ABC in the x-axis and call the image $A_1B_1C_1$.

b) Reflect triangle $A_1B_1C_1$ in the y-axis and call the image $A_2B_2C_2$.

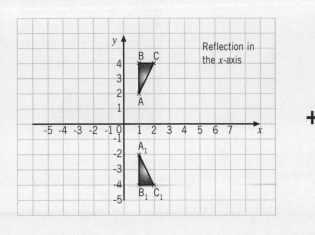

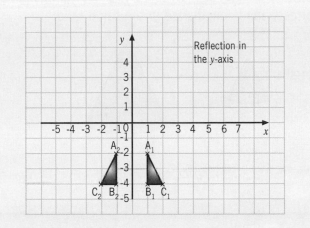

+

The single transformation that maps ABC directly onto $A_2B_2C_2$ is a rotation of $180°$ about centre $(0, 0)$.

=

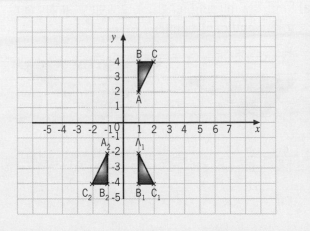

Quick test

1 Draw an enlargement of shape P with a scale factor of 2. Call it P_1.

2 a) Rotate the shaded shape through a $90°$ clockwise rotation about $(0, 0)$. Call this shape B.

b) Reflect shape B in the x-axis and call this shape C.

1

2

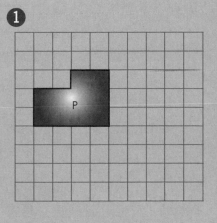

Similarity & congruency

Similar figures

Similar figures are those that are the same shape but different sizes. Corresponding angles are equal. Corresponding lengths are in the same ratio. For example:

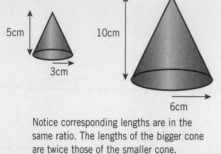

Notice corresponding lengths are in the same ratio. The lengths of the bigger cone are twice those of the smaller cone.

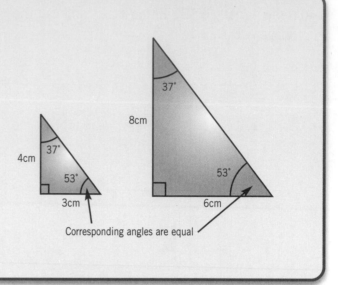

Corresponding angles are equal

Finding missing lengths of similar figures

Examples

a) Find the missing length a, giving your answer to 2 significant figures.

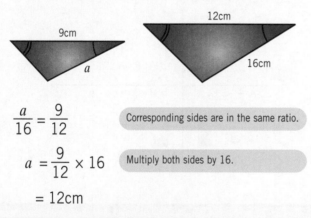

$$\frac{a}{16} = \frac{9}{12}$$

Corresponding sides are in the same ratio.

$$a = \frac{9}{12} \times 16$$

Multiply both sides by 16.

$$= 12\text{cm}$$

b) Calculate the missing length x.

$$\frac{x}{6} = \frac{24}{16}$$

Corresponding sides are in the same ratio.

$$x = \frac{24}{16} \times 6$$

Multiply both sides by 6.

$$= 9\text{cm}$$

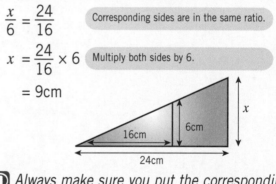

Always make sure you put the corresponding sides in the correct order and remember that whatever you are trying to work out must go on the top of the fraction.

Congruent triangles

Two triangles are congruent if one of the following sets of conditions is true (S stands for side, A for angle, R for right angle, H for hypotenuse):

SSS – The three sides of one triangle are the same lengths as the three sides of the other.

SAS – Two sides and the angle between them (included angle) in one triangle are equal to two sides and the included angle in the other.

RHS – Each triangle contains a right angle. The hypotenuse and another pair of sides are equal.

AAS – Two angles and a side in one triangle are equal to two angles and the corresponding side in the other.

SAS   AAS

Areas and volumes of similar figures

Areas of similar figures are not in the same ratio as their lengths. For example, the corresponding lengths of these squares are in the ratio 1 : 2 but their areas are in the ratio 1 : 4.

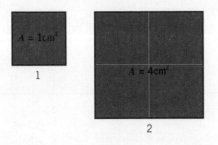

If the corresponding lengths are in the ratio $a : b$, their areas are in the ratio $a^2 : b^2$.

A similar result can be found when looking at the volumes of similar objects: if the corresponding lengths are in the ratio $a : b$, their volumes are in the ratio $a^3 : b^3$.

For a scale factor n:
- **The sides are n times bigger.**
- **The area is n^2 times bigger.**
- **The volume is n^3 times bigger.**

Examples

a) These two shapes are similar. If the area of the smaller shape is 12cm², calculate the area of the larger shape.

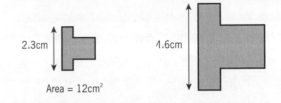

The linear scale factor is 2.3 : 4.6 = 1 : 2
Area scale factor is $1^2 : 2^2$ = 1 : 4
Area of larger shape = 4 × 12 = 48cm²

b) Two cones have surface areas of 9cm² and 25cm². Find the ratio of their volumes.

The area ratio is 9 : 25
so $a^2 : b^2$ = $3^2 : 5^2$
i.e. $a : b$ = 3 : 5

Volume ratio $a^3 : b^3$ = $3^3 : 5^3$
                             =   27 : 125

🄾 *When finding the area and volume of similar figures, always try to work out the linear scale factor. Once you have calculated this, the rest should be easy. If you are given the area or volume scale factor, you may need to take the square or cube root to find the linear scale factor.*

Quick test

1 Find the lengths labelled by the letter x in these similar shapes. 🖩

a)

b)

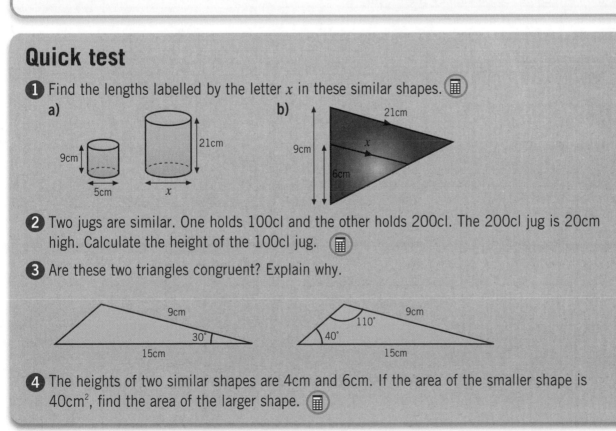

2 Two jugs are similar. One holds 100cl and the other holds 200cl. The 200cl jug is 20cm high. Calculate the height of the 100cl jug. 🖩

3 Are these two triangles congruent? Explain why.

4 The heights of two similar shapes are 4cm and 6cm. If the area of the smaller shape is 40cm², find the area of the larger shape. 🖩

Loci & coordinates in 3D

Common loci

The **locus** of a point is the set of all the possible positions which that point can occupy, subject to some given condition or rule. The plural of locus is **loci**.

Remember these points:

The locus of the points that are equidistant from a fixed point P is a circle.	The locus of the points that are equidistant from two non-parallel lines is the line that bisects the angle formed by the two lines.
The locus of the points that are equidistant from two points, X and Y, is the perpendicular bisector of XY.	The locus of the points that are a constant distance from a line is a pair of parallel lines above and below the line.
	The locus of the points that are equidistant from a line segment XY is a pair of parallel lines above and below XY, with semicircles at either end.

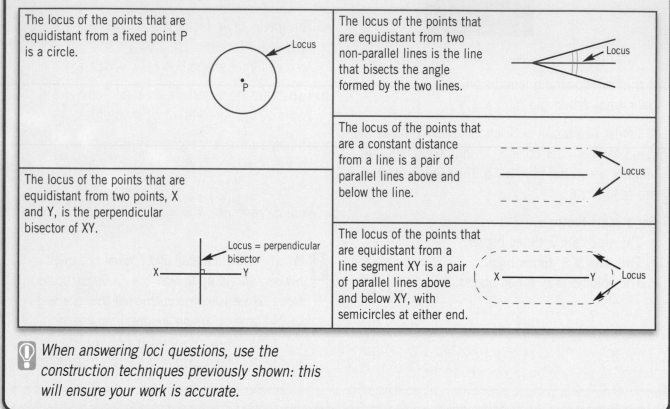

When answering loci questions, use the construction techniques previously shown: this will ensure your work is accurate.

Coordinates in 3D

Coordinates in 3D involve the extension of the normal x and y-axes into a third direction, known as the z-axis. All positions then have three coordinates (x, y, z).

For example, for the cuboid opposite the vertices would have the following (x, y, z) coordinates:

A (3, 0, 0)   E (0, 0, 1)
B (3, 2, 0)   F (3, 0, 1)
C (0, 2, 0)   G (3, 2, 1)
D (0, 2, 1)   O (0, 0, 0)

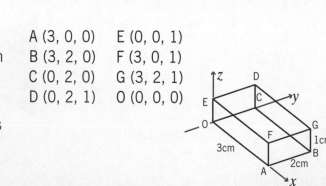

Quick test

① A gold coin is buried in the rectangular field. It is 4m from T and equidistant from RU and RS. Copy the diagram to a scale of 1cm : 1m and mark with an X the position of the gold coin.

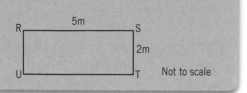

Angle properties of circles

Circle theorems

There are several circle theorems you need to know and be able to apply. The theorems are:

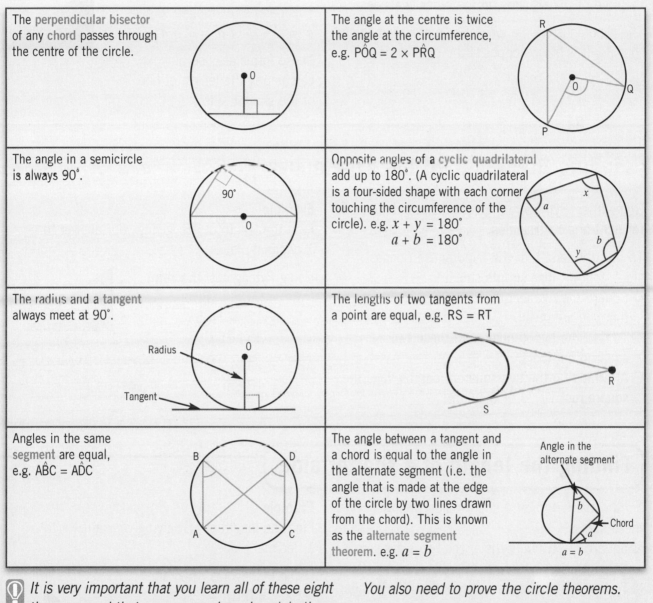

The perpendicular bisector of any chord passes through the centre of the circle.

The angle at the centre is twice the angle at the circumference, e.g. $P\hat{O}Q = 2 \times P\hat{R}Q$

The angle in a semicircle is always 90°.

Opposite angles of a cyclic quadrilateral add up to 180°. (A cyclic quadrilateral is a four-sided shape with each corner touching the circumference of the circle). e.g. $x + y = 180°$
$$a + b = 180°$$

The radius and a tangent always meet at 90°.

Radius

Tangent

The lengths of two tangents from a point are equal, e.g. RS = RT

Angles in the same segment are equal, e.g. $A\hat{B}C = A\hat{D}C$

The angle between a tangent and a chord is equal to the angle in the alternate segment (i.e. the angle that is made at the edge of the circle by two lines drawn from the chord). This is known as the alternate segment theorem. e.g. $a = b$

Angle in the alternate segment

Chord

$a = b$

It is very important that you learn all of these eight theorems and that you can apply and explain them.

You also need to prove the circle theorems.

Quick test

1 Calculate the missing angles in the diagram.

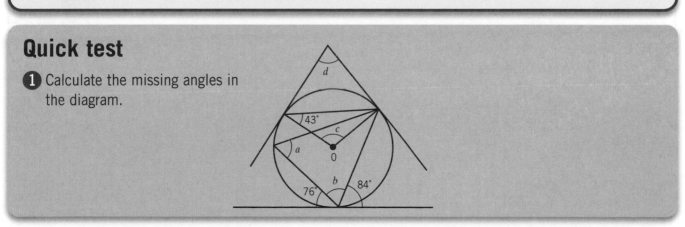

Pythagoras' theorem

The theorem

Pythagoras' theorem states: in any right-angled triangle, the square on the hypotenuse is equal to the sum of the squares on the other two sides.

The hypotenuse is the longest side of a right-angled triangle. It is always opposite the right angle.

Using the letters in the diagram, the theorem is written as $c^2 = a^2 + b^2$

This can be rearranged to give $a^2 = c^2 - b^2$ or $b^2 = c^2 - a^2$

These forms are useful when calculating the length of one of the shorter sides.

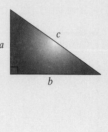

Finding the length of the hypotenuse

Remember: Pythagoras' theorem can only be used for right-angled triangles.

To find the length of the hypotenuse (longest side), follow these simple steps:
❶ Square the two lengths of the two shorter sides that you are given.
❷ To find the hypotenuse, add these two squared numbers.
❸ After adding the two squared lengths, take the **square root** $(\sqrt{})$ of the sum.

Example
Find the length of AB, giving your answer to 1 decimal place.

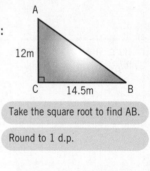

Using Pythagoras' theorem:
$$(AB)^2 = (AC)^2 + (BC)^2$$
$$= 12^2 + 14.5^2$$
$$= 354.25$$
$$AB = \sqrt{354.25}$$
$$= 18.8m$$

Take the square root to find AB.

Round to 1 d.p.

Finding the length of a shorter side

To find the length of a shorter side, follow these steps:
❶ Square the two lengths of the two sides you are given.
❷ To find the shorter length, subtract the smaller value from the larger value.
❸ Take the square root $(\sqrt{})$ of your answer.

 Pythagoras' theorem allows us to calculate the length of one of the sides of a right-angled triangle when the other two sides are known. If you are not told to what degree of accuracy to round your answer, be guided by significant figures given in the question.

Example
Find the length of FG, giving your answer to 1 decimal place.

Using Pythagoras' theorem:
$$(EF)^2 = (EG)^2 + (FG)^2$$
$$(FG)^2 = (EF)^2 - (EG)^2$$
$$= 27^2 - 18^2$$
$$= 405$$
$$FG = \sqrt{405}$$
$$= 20.1cm$$

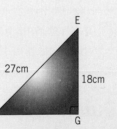

Calculating the length of a line AB, given two sets of coordinates

By drawing in a triangle between the two points A (1, 2) and B (7, 6) we can find the length of AB by Pythagoras' theorem.

Horizontal distance = 6   [7 – 1]
Vertical distance = 4   [6 – 2]

$$\text{Length of } (AB)^2 = 6^2 + 4^2$$
$$= 36 + 16$$
$$= 52$$
$$AB = \sqrt{52}$$

Length of AB = 7.21 (2 d.p.)

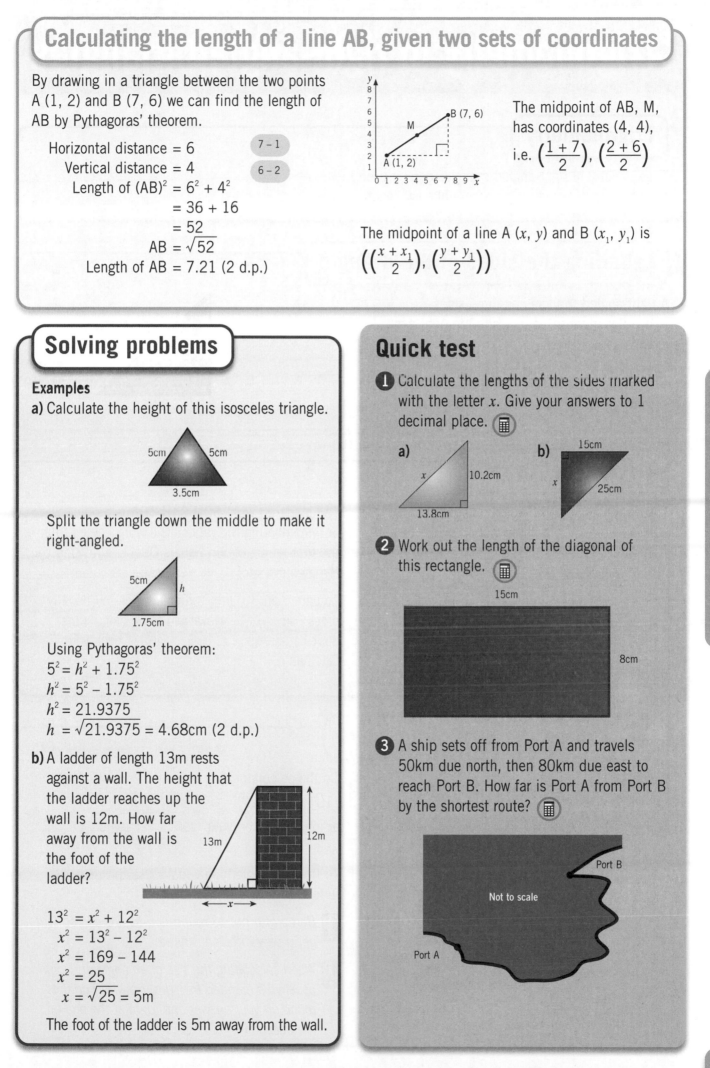

The midpoint of AB, M, has coordinates (4, 4),

i.e. $\left(\dfrac{1+7}{2}\right), \left(\dfrac{2+6}{2}\right)$

The midpoint of a line A (x, y) and B (x_1, y_1) is

$$\left(\left(\dfrac{x + x_1}{2}\right), \left(\dfrac{y + y_1}{2}\right)\right)$$

Solving problems

Examples

a) Calculate the height of this isosceles triangle.

5cm   5cm
3.5cm

Split the triangle down the middle to make it right-angled.

5cm h
1.75cm

Using Pythagoras' theorem:
$$5^2 = h^2 + 1.75^2$$
$$h^2 = 5^2 - 1.75^2$$
$$h^2 = 21.9375$$
$$h = \sqrt{21.9375} = 4.68\text{cm (2 d.p.)}$$

b) A ladder of length 13m rests against a wall. The height that the ladder reaches up the wall is 12m. How far away from the wall is the foot of the ladder?

13m   12m

$$13^2 = x^2 + 12^2$$
$$x^2 = 13^2 - 12^2$$
$$x^2 = 169 - 144$$
$$x^2 = 25$$
$$x = \sqrt{25} = 5\text{m}$$

The foot of the ladder is 5m away from the wall.

Quick test

1 Calculate the lengths of the sides marked with the letter x. Give your answers to 1 decimal place. 🔢

a)
x 10.2cm
13.8cm

b)
15cm
x 25cm

2 Work out the length of the diagonal of this rectangle. 🔢

15cm
8cm

3 A ship sets off from Port A and travels 50km due north, then 80km due east to reach Port B. How far is Port A from Port B by the shortest route? 🔢

Port B
Not to scale
Port A

Trigonometry in right-angled triangles

Trigonometry

Trigonometry in right-angled triangles can be used to calculate an unknown angle or an unknown length.

Labelling the sides of the triangle

A right-angled triangle has three sides:
- **hyp** (**hypotenuse**) is opposite the right angle.
- **opp** (opposite side) is opposite the angle θ.
- **adj** (adjacent side) is next to the angle θ.
  θ is a Greek letter called **theta** and is often used to represent **angles**.

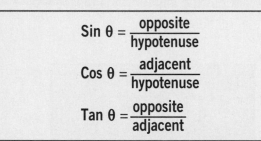

Trigonometric ratios

The three trigonometric ratios are **sine** (usually abbreviated to sin), **cosine** (cos) and **tangent** (tan):

$$\text{Sin } \theta = \frac{\text{opposite}}{\text{hypotenuse}}$$

$$\text{Cos } \theta = \frac{\text{adjacent}}{\text{hypotenuse}}$$

$$\text{Tan } \theta = \frac{\text{opposite}}{\text{adjacent}}$$

The made-up word **SOH CAH TOA** is a quick way of remembering the ratios. The word comes from the first letters of **S**in equals **O**pposite divided by **H**ypotenuse, etc.

To enter 'sin 30' into the calculator you usually press | sin | | 30 |. However, some calculators do it backwards, i.e. | 30 | | sin |. Check your calculator.

Calculating the size of an angle

You may have an | Inv | key on your calculator.

Example

Calculate angle ABC.

$$\text{Tan } \theta = \frac{\text{opp}}{\text{adj}}$$ Label the sides and decide which ratio you need.

$$\text{Tan } \theta = \frac{15}{27}$$ Divide the top value by the bottom value.

$$\text{Tan } \theta = 0.\dot{5}$$

$$\theta = 29.1° \text{ (1 d.p.)}$$

On the calculator, key in

| 15 | | ÷ | | 27 | | = | | shift | | tan | | = |

or, depending on your type of calculator:

| shift | | tan | | 15 | | ÷ | | 27 | | = |

To find the angle, you usually use the second function on your calculator.

🛈 *Be careful not to round $0.\dot{5}$ to 0.6 as you will get a very different answer.*

🛈 *When calculating the size of an angle, it should usually be rounded to 1 d.p. However, do not round off your answer until right at the end of the question.*

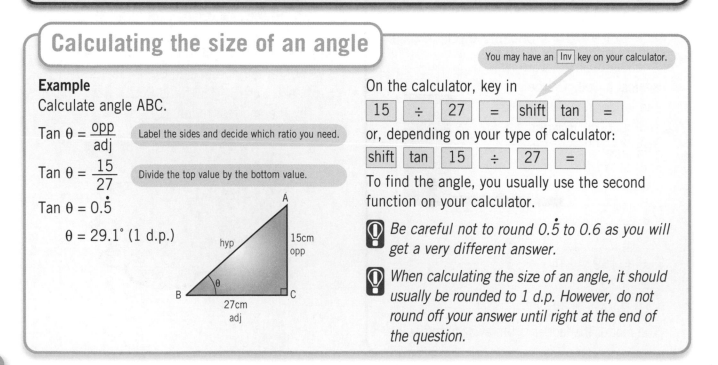

Calculating the length of a side

Examples

a) Calculate the length of BC.

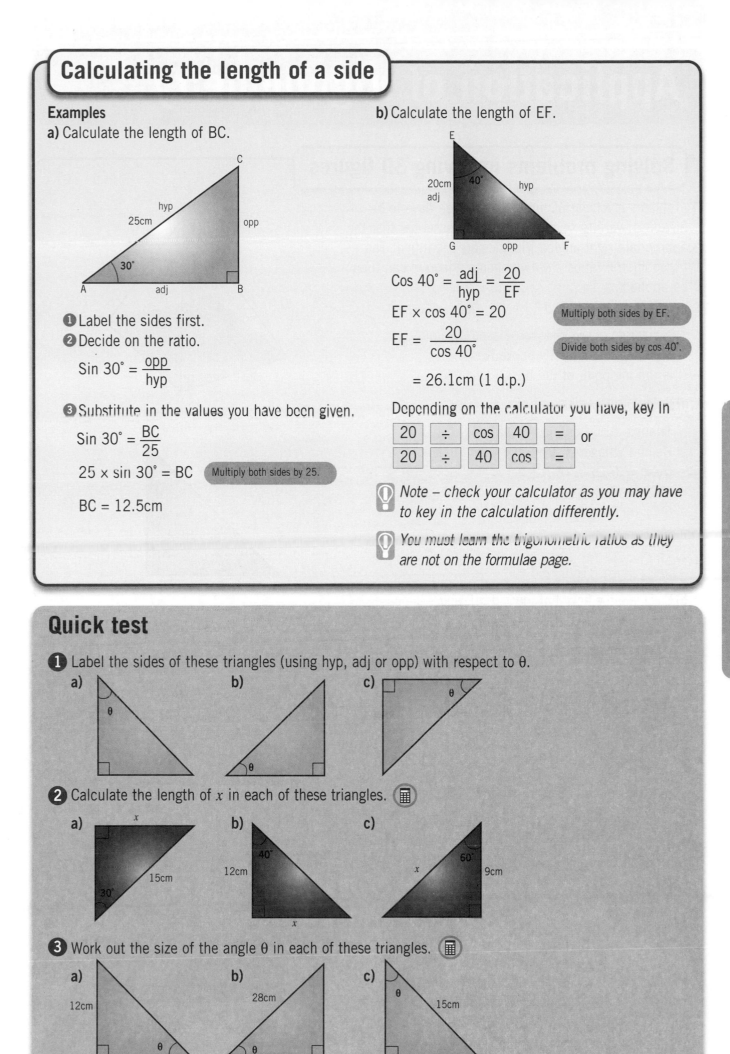

❶ Label the sides first.
❷ Decide on the ratio.

$$\text{Sin } 30° = \frac{\text{opp}}{\text{hyp}}$$

❸ Substitute in the values you have been given.

$$\text{Sin } 30° = \frac{BC}{25}$$

$$25 \times \sin 30° = BC \quad \boxed{\text{Multiply both sides by 25.}}$$

$$BC = 12.5\text{cm}$$

b) Calculate the length of EF.

$$\text{Cos } 40° = \frac{\text{adj}}{\text{hyp}} = \frac{20}{EF}$$

$$EF \times \cos 40° = 20 \quad \boxed{\text{Multiply both sides by EF.}}$$

$$EF = \frac{20}{\cos 40°} \quad \boxed{\text{Divide both sides by cos 40°.}}$$

$$= 26.1\text{cm (1 d.p.)}$$

Depending on the calculator you have, key in

| 20 | ÷ | cos | 40 | = | or |

| 20 | ÷ | 40 | cos | = |

🛈 *Note – check your calculator as you may have to key in the calculation differently.*

🛈 *You must learn the trigonometric ratios as they are not on the formulae page.*

Quick test

❶ Label the sides of these triangles (using hyp, adj or opp) with respect to θ.

a)   b)   c)

❷ Calculate the length of x in each of these triangles. 🖩

a)   b)   c)

❸ Work out the size of the angle θ in each of these triangles. 🖩

a)   b)   c)

Application of trigonometry

Solving problems involving 3D figures

Problems involving 3D figures very often have to be broken down into several stages. It is essential that the appropriate right-angled triangles are identified. The trigonometric ratios and Pythagoras' theorem can then be applied.

Example

The diagram shows a square-based pyramid.
The point E lies directly above N.
N is the midpoint of the base.

a) Calculate the distance AC.

Triangle ADC contains a right angle at D.
Using Pythagoras' theorem:
$(AC)^2 = (AD)^2 + (DC)^2$
$(AC)^2 = 8^2 + 8^2$
$(AC)^2 = 64 + 64$
$(AC)^2 = 128$
$AC = \sqrt{128}$
$AC = 11.31cm$ (2 d.p.)

b) Calculate the height of the vertex E above the base.

Triangle ENC contains a right angle at N.
Using Pythagoras' theorem:
$(EC)^2 = (EN)^2 + (NC)^2$
$(EN)^2 = (EC)^2 - (NC)^2$
$(EN)^2 = 20^2 - 5.65^2...$ (Since NC $= \frac{1}{2}$ AC $= \frac{11.31...}{2}$)
$(EN)^2 = 400 - 32$
$EN = \sqrt{368}$
$EN = 19.18...cm$
The vertex E is 19.18cm above the base of the pyramid.

c) Calculate the angle between EC and the base ABCD.

Triangle ENC contains a right angle at N.
$\text{Cos } \theta = \dfrac{adj}{hyp} = \dfrac{5.65...}{20}$
$\theta = \cos^{-1}\left(\dfrac{5.65...}{20}\right)$
$= 73.6°$ (1 d.p.)

Check that you know how to use your calculator for trigonometry questions. It is helpful to draw the individual triangle that you are using – this will allow you to label it properly.

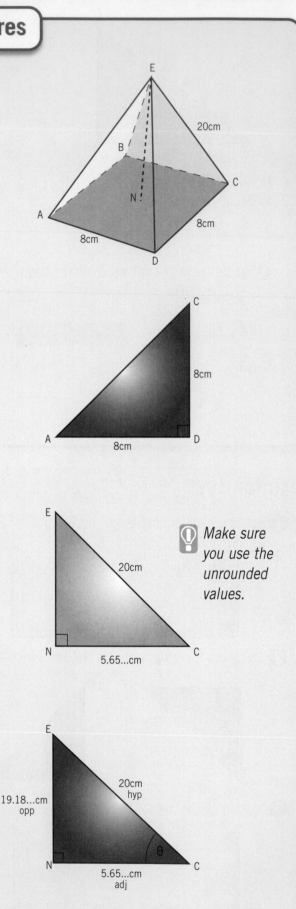

Make sure you use the unrounded values.

Finding the length of a diagonal in a cuboid

The length of the diagonal of a cuboid of dimensions abc is found by applying Pythagoras' theorem twice.

$$x^2 = c^2 + y^2$$
$$y^2 = a^2 + b^2$$
So $x^2 = c^2 + (a^2 + b^2)$

The length x of the longest diagonal in a cuboid with dimensions $a \times b \times c$ is:
$$x^2 = a^2 + b^2 + c^2$$

This is a 3D version of Pythagoras' theorem.

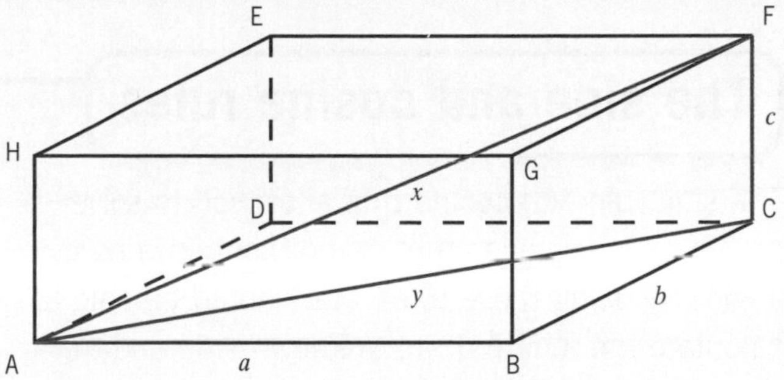

Angles of elevation and depression

The angle of elevation is measured from the horizontal **upwards**.

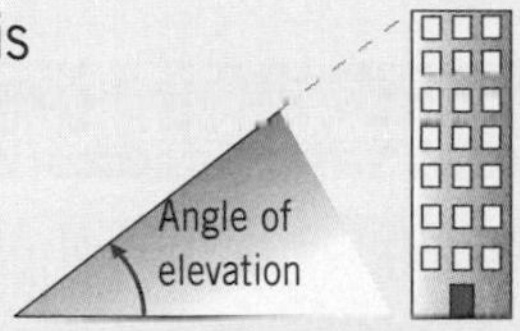

The angle of depression is measured from the horizontal **downwards**.

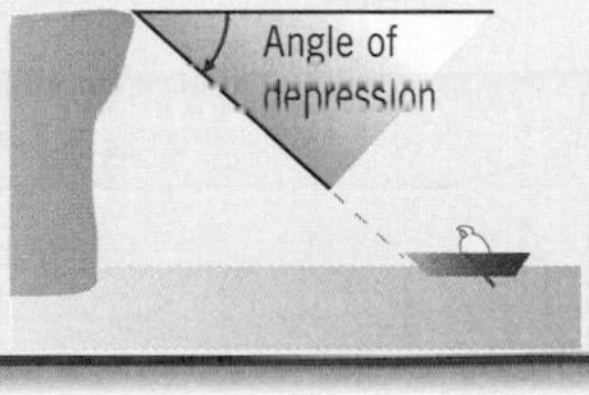

Bearings and trigonometry

Example

In the diagram, A, B and C represent three towns. The distance AB is 16km. The distance BC is 9km. Work out the bearing of B from A.

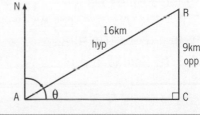

The required bearing is from the north at A. Find angle BAC.

$$\text{Sin } \theta = \frac{\text{opp}}{\text{hyp}} = \frac{9}{16}$$

$$\theta = \sin^{-1}\frac{9}{16}$$

$$= 34.2° \text{ (1 d.p.)}$$

Bearing of B from A is $90° - 34.2° = 55.8°$
$$= 055.8° \text{ or } 056°$$

Quick test

1 Dipak stands 30m from the base of a tower. He measures the angle of elevation from ground level to the top of the tower as 50°. Calculate the height of the tower. Give your answer to 3 significant figures. 🖩

2 In the triangle opposite... 🖩
a) calculate the length of BN
b) calculate the length of BC
c) calculate the size of angle BCN.

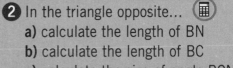

3 The diagram shows a cuboid. Calculate... 🖩
a) the length of HF
b) angle CHF.

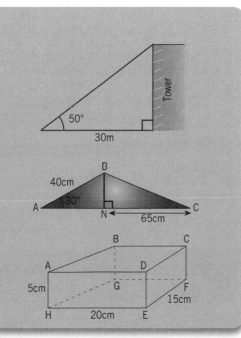

Further trigonometry

The sine and cosine rules

The sine rule and cosine rule allow you to solve problems in triangles that do not contain a right angle. By using these rules, you should be able to calculate the length of an unknown side and the size of an unknown angle.

Labelling the triangle

When labelling the triangle side a is opposite angle A, side b is opposite angle B, etc.

The sine rule

$$\frac{a}{\sin A} = \frac{b}{\sin B} = \frac{c}{\sin C}$$

or

$$\frac{\sin A}{a} = \frac{\sin B}{b} = \frac{\sin C}{c}$$

The cosine rule

$$a^2 = b^2 + c^2 - 2bc \cos A$$

or

$$\cos A = \frac{b^2 + c^2 - a^2}{2bc}$$

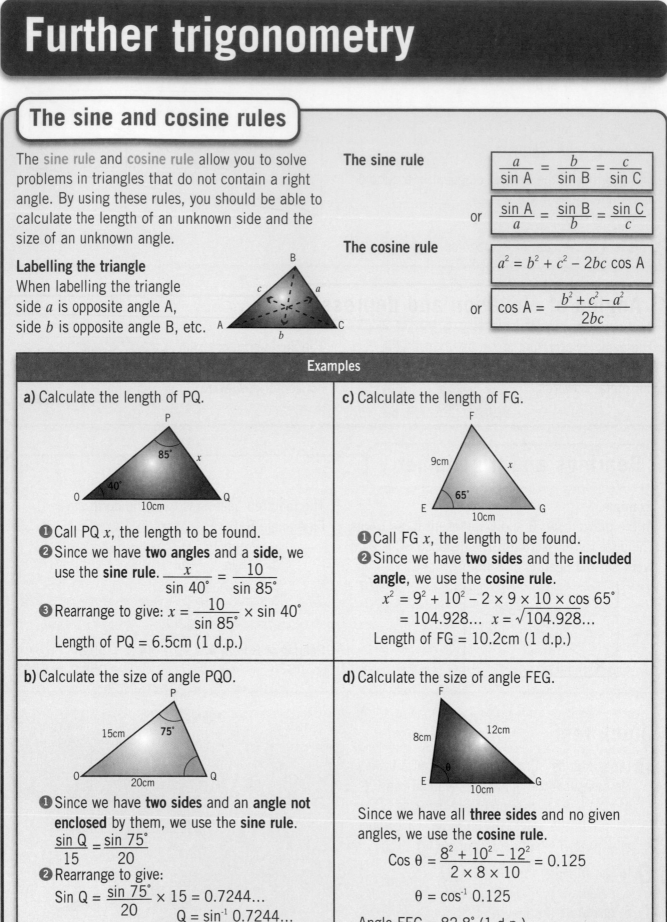

Examples

a) Calculate the length of PQ.

❶ Call PQ x, the length to be found.
❷ Since we have **two angles** and a **side**, we use the **sine rule**. $\dfrac{x}{\sin 40°} = \dfrac{10}{\sin 85°}$
❸ Rearrange to give: $x = \dfrac{10}{\sin 85°} \times \sin 40°$
Length of PQ = 6.5cm (1 d.p.)

c) Calculate the length of FG.

❶ Call FG x, the length to be found.
❷ Since we have **two sides** and the **included angle**, we use the **cosine rule**.
$$x^2 = 9^2 + 10^2 - 2 \times 9 \times 10 \times \cos 65°$$
$$= 104.928... \quad x = \sqrt{104.928...}$$
Length of FG = 10.2cm (1 d.p.)

b) Calculate the size of angle PQO.

❶ Since we have **two sides** and an **angle not enclosed** by them, we use the **sine rule**.
$$\frac{\sin Q}{15} = \frac{\sin 75°}{20}$$
❷ Rearrange to give:
$$\text{Sin } Q = \frac{\sin 75°}{20} \times 15 = 0.7244...$$
$$Q = \sin^{-1} 0.7244...$$
Angle PQO = 46.4° (1 d.p.)

d) Calculate the size of angle FEG.

Since we have all **three sides** and no given angles, we use the **cosine rule**.
$$\text{Cos } \theta = \frac{8^2 + 10^2 - 12^2}{2 \times 8 \times 10} = 0.125$$
$$\theta = \cos^{-1} 0.125$$
Angle FEG = 82.8° (1 d.p.)

The sine and cosine rules are key topics at GCSE. They are usually worth a lot of marks and the key to success is to learn when to use the different rules. If in doubt and you have time, try out both the sine and cosine rules on your triangle; you should find that one of them will not work.

Graphs of trigonometric functions

The behaviour of the sine, cosine and tangent functions may be represented graphically as shown below.

$y = \sin x$

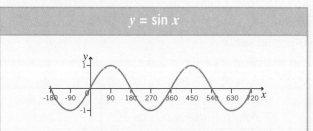

The maximum and minimum values of sin x are 1 and -1. The pattern repeats every 360°.

$y = \cos x$

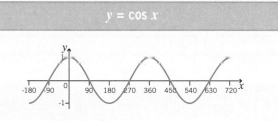

The maximum and minimum values of cos x are 1 and -1. The pattern repeats every 360°. This graph is the same as $y = \sin x$ except it has been moved 90° to the left.

$y = \tan x$

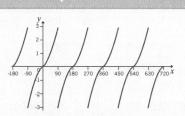

This graph is nothing like the two above. The values of tan x repeat every 180°. The tan of 90° is infinity, i.e. a value so great it cannot be written down.

> Practise drawing the trigonometric graphs. You could be asked to sketch them in the exam.

The graph transformations (see page 51) can be applied to trigonometric curves.

$y = a \sin x$

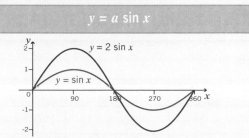

Here the points are stretched outwards in the y direction if $a > 1$, as the y coordinates are increased. If $a < 1$, they are pushed inwards, as the y coordinates do not go as high.

$y = \sin (bx)$

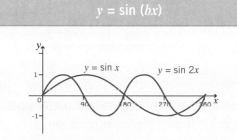

Here the points are stretched by a scale factor of $\frac{1}{b}$ parallel to the x-axis.

The trigonometric graphs can be used to solve inverse problems.

Example

Solve sin $x = 0.5$ for values of x between 0° and 360°.

Draw a straight line across the graph at $y = 0.5$ and by its symmetrical properties you can see that the solutions are:

$x = 30°$ and 150°. (390° is out of the range)

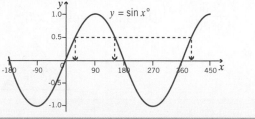

Quick test

1 Calculate the missing length or angle marked x in these triangles. ▦

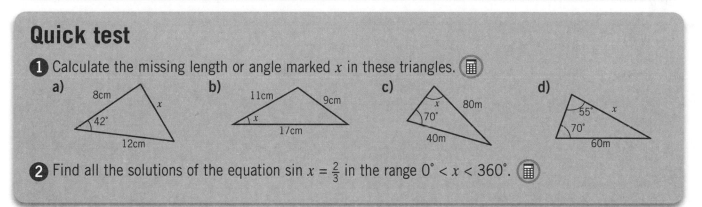

2 Find all the solutions of the equation sin $x = \frac{2}{3}$ in the range 0° < x < 360°. ▦

Measures & measurement

Metric and imperial units

Metric units

Length	Weight	Capacity
10mm = 1cm	1000mg = 1g	1000ml = 1 litre
100cm = 1m	1000g = 1kg	100cl = 1 litre
1000m = 1km	1000kg = 1 tonne	$1000cm^3$ = 1 litre

Imperial units

Length	Weight	Capacity
1 foot = 12 inches	1 stone = 14 pounds (lb)	20 fluid oz = 1 pint
1 yard = 3 feet	1 pound = 16 ounces (oz)	8 pints = 1 gallon

Compound measures

Speed

Speed can be measured in kilometres per hour (km/h), miles per hour (mph) and metres per second (m/s). Km/h, mph and m/s are all **compound measures** because they involve a combination of basic measures.

$$\text{Average speed} = \frac{\text{total distance travelled}}{\text{total time taken}}$$

$$s = \frac{d}{t}$$

Always check the units before starting a question. Change them if necessary.

From the speed formula, two other formulae can be found.

$$\text{Time} = \frac{\text{distance}}{\text{speed}} \qquad \text{Distance} = \text{speed} \times \text{time}$$

$$s = \frac{d}{t} \qquad t = \frac{d}{s} \qquad d = st$$

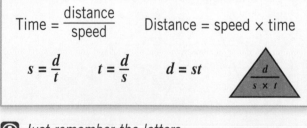

🛈 *Just remember the letters.*

Density

$$\textbf{Density} = \frac{\text{mass}}{\text{volume}} \qquad \text{Volume} = \frac{\text{mass}}{\text{density}}$$

$$\text{Mass} = \text{density} \times \text{volume}$$

$$D = \frac{M}{V} \qquad V = \frac{M}{D} \qquad M = DV$$

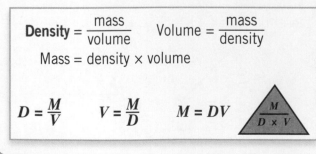

Examples

a) A car travels 50 miles in 1 hour 20 minutes. Find the speed in miles per hour.

Change the time units first:

20 minutes = $\frac{20}{60}$ of 1 hour

$$s = \frac{d}{t} = \frac{50}{1\frac{20}{60}} = 37.5\text{mph}$$

b) A car travels a distance of 240 miles at an average speed of 65mph. How long does it take?

$$\text{Time} = \frac{\text{distance}}{\text{speed}}, \text{ so } t = \frac{240}{65} = 3.692 \text{ hours}$$

3.692 hours must be changed into hours and minutes, so follow these steps:

❶ Subtract the hours: 3.692 − 3 = 0.692

❷ Multiply the decimal part by 60 minutes.
   0.692 × 60 = 42 minutes (nearest minute)
   So time taken = 3 hours 42 minutes

c) Find the density of an object whose mass is 400g and whose volume is $25cm^3$.

$$\text{Density} = \frac{M}{V} = \frac{400}{25} = 16\text{g/cm}^3$$

Since the mass is in grams and the volume is in cm^3, density is in g/cm^3.

Comparisons between metric and imperial units

Length	Weight	Capacity
2.5cm ≈ 1 inch	25g ≈ 1 ounce	1 litre ≈ $1\frac{3}{4}$ pints
30cm ≈ 1 foot	1kg ≈ 2.2 pounds	4.5 litres ≈ 1 gallon
1m ≈ 39 inches		
8km ≈ 5 miles		

Comparisons between metric and imperial units are only approximate.

Example
Change 25km into miles.

8km ≈ 5 miles
1km ≈ $\frac{5}{8}$ mile = 0.625 miles
25km ≈ 25 × 0.625
　　 = 15.625 miles

There is a lot of learning to do in this section. Try to learn all the metric and imperial conversions, and the formulae for speed, distance and time.

Accuracy of measurement

There are two types of measurements – discrete measurements and continuous measurements:

- **Discrete measures** are quantities that can be counted; for example, the number of baked bean tins on a shelf.
- **Continuous measures** are measurements that have been made using a measuring instrument; for example, the height of a person. Continuous measures are not exact.

For example, Nigel weighs 72kg to the nearest kg. His actual weight could be anywhere between 71.5kg and 72.5kg.

If W represents weight, then:

$$71.5 \leqslant W < 72.5$$

This is the **lower limit** of Nigel's weight (sometimes known as the **lower bound**). Anything below 71.5 would be recorded as 71kg.

This is the **upper limit** (**upper bound**) of Nigel's weight. Anything from 72.5 upwards would be recorded as 73kg.

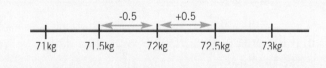

Quick test

1. Change 3500g into kilograms.

2. Change 3kg into pounds.

3. Change 6 litres into pints.

4. Write down the upper and lower limits for a time of 9.2 seconds, rounded to the nearest tenth of a second.

5. Write down the upper and lower limits for a weight of 58kg, rounded to the nearest kilogram.

6. Amy walks 6 miles in 2 hours 40 minutes. Find her average speed. 🖩

7. Find the time taken for a car to travel 600 miles at an average speed of 70mph. 🖩

8. Find the density of an object whose mass is 20g and whose volume is 9cm³. 🖩

Area of 2D shapes

Perimeter and area of 2D shapes

The perimeter is the distance around the outside edge of a shape.

The area is the amount of space a 2D shape covers.

Common units of area are square millimetres (mm^2), square centimetres (cm^2), square metres (m^2), etc.

Areas of quadrilaterals and triangles

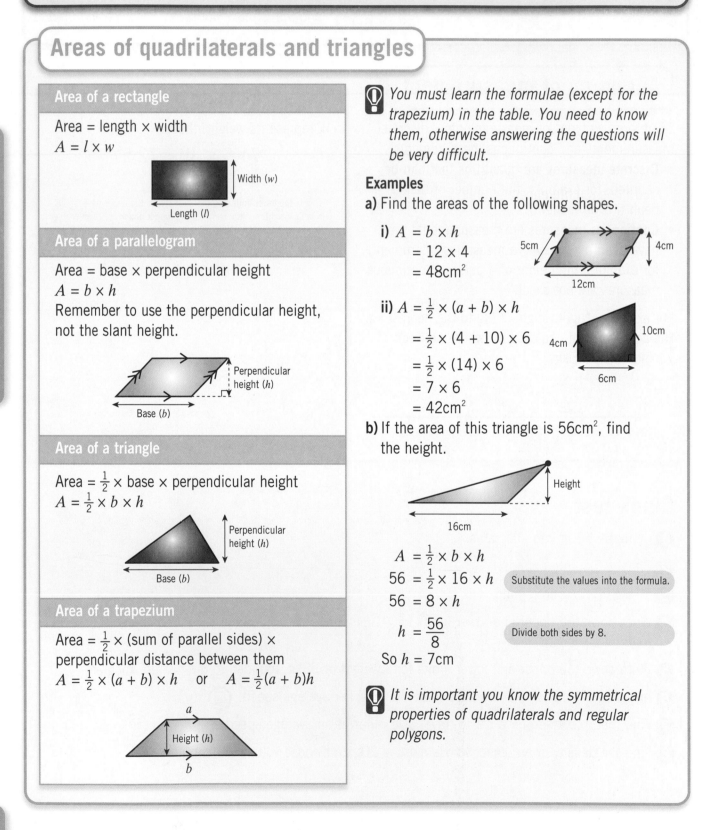

Area of a rectangle

Area = length × width
$A = l \times w$

Width (w)
Length (l)

Area of a parallelogram

Area = base × perpendicular height
$A = b \times h$
Remember to use the perpendicular height, not the slant height.

Perpendicular height (h)
Base (b)

Area of a triangle

Area = $\frac{1}{2}$ × base × perpendicular height
$A = \frac{1}{2} \times b \times h$

Perpendicular height (h)
Base (b)

Area of a trapezium

Area = $\frac{1}{2}$ × (sum of parallel sides) × perpendicular distance between them
$A = \frac{1}{2} \times (a + b) \times h$ or $A = \frac{1}{2}(a + b)h$

a
Height (h)
b

> You must learn the formulae (except for the trapezium) in the table. You need to know them, otherwise answering the questions will be very difficult.

Examples

a) Find the areas of the following shapes.

i) $A = b \times h$
$= 12 \times 4$
$= 48cm^2$

5cm 4cm
12cm

ii) $A = \frac{1}{2} \times (a + b) \times h$
$= \frac{1}{2} \times (4 + 10) \times 6$
$= \frac{1}{2} \times (14) \times 6$
$= 7 \times 6$
$= 42cm^2$

4cm 10cm
6cm

b) If the area of this triangle is $56cm^2$, find the height.

Height
16cm

$A = \frac{1}{2} \times b \times h$
$56 = \frac{1}{2} \times 16 \times h$ Substitute the values into the formula.
$56 = 8 \times h$
$h = \dfrac{56}{8}$ Divide both sides by 8.
So $h = 7cm$

> It is important you know the symmetrical properties of quadrilaterals and regular polygons.

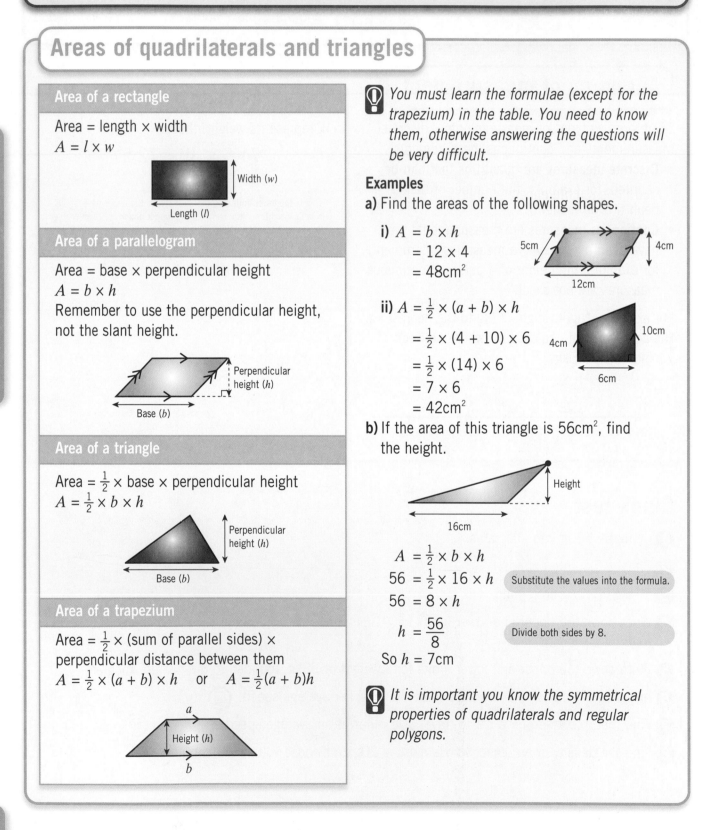

Geometry and measures

Changing area units

This example will help you to change area units.

The square has a length of 1m. This is the same as a length of 100cm.

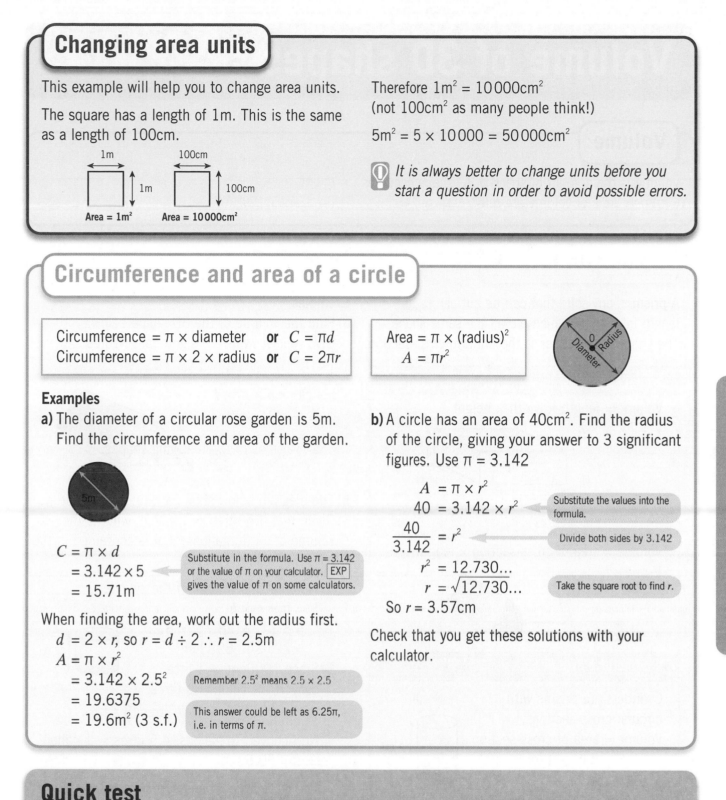

Area = 1m²   Area = 10000cm²

Therefore 1m² = 10000cm²
(not 100cm² as many people think!)

5m² = 5 × 10000 = 50000cm²

💡 *It is always better to change units before you start a question in order to avoid possible errors.*

Circumference and area of a circle

Circumference = π × diameter   **or** $C = \pi d$
Circumference = π × 2 × radius **or** $C = 2\pi r$

Area = π × (radius)²
$A = \pi r^2$

Examples

a) The diameter of a circular rose garden is 5m. Find the circumference and area of the garden.

5m

$C = \pi \times d$
  $= 3.142 \times 5$
  $= 15.71$m

Substitute in the formula. Use π = 3.142 or the value of π on your calculator. [EXP] gives the value of π on some calculators.

When finding the area, work out the radius first.
$d = 2 \times r$, so $r = d \div 2$ ∴ $r = 2.5$m
$A = \pi \times r^2$
  $= 3.142 \times 2.5^2$ Remember 2.5² means 2.5 × 2.5
  $= 19.6375$
  $= 19.6$m² (3 s.f.)   This answer could be left as 6.25π, i.e. in terms of π.

b) A circle has an area of 40cm². Find the radius of the circle, giving your answer to 3 significant figures. Use π = 3.142

$A = \pi \times r^2$
$40 = 3.142 \times r^2$ Substitute the values into the formula.

$\dfrac{40}{3.142} = r^2$ Divide both sides by 3.142

$r^2 = 12.730...$
$r = \sqrt{12.730...}$ Take the square root to find r.

So $r = 3.57$cm

Check that you get these solutions with your calculator.

Quick test

1 Work out the areas of these shapes, giving your answers to 3 significant figures where appropriate. Use the π button on your calculator where appropriate.

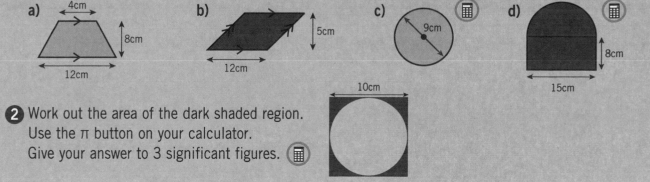

a) 4cm, 8cm, 12cm
b) 5cm, 12cm
c) 9cm
d) 8cm, 15cm

2 Work out the area of the dark shaded region. Use the π button on your calculator. Give your answer to 3 significant figures.

10cm

Volume of 3D shapes

Volume

Volume is the amount of space a 3D shape occupies.
Common units of volume are mm³, cm³, m³, etc.

Volume of prisms

A **prism** is any solid that can be cut across its length into slices, which are all the same shape. The shape of the slices is the uniform cross-section.

Volume of a cuboid

Volume = length × width × height
$V = l \times w \times h$

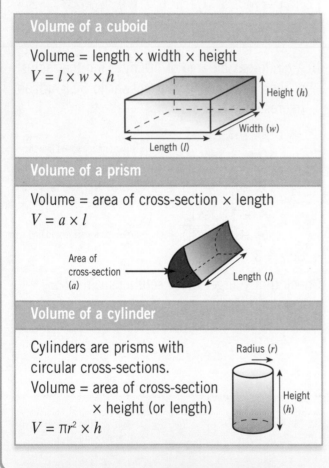

Height (*h*)
Width (*w*)
Length (*l*)

Volume of a prism

Volume = area of cross-section × length
$V = a \times l$

Area of cross-section (*a*)
Length (*l*)

Volume of a cylinder

Cylinders are prisms with circular cross-sections.
Volume = area of cross-section × height (or length)
$V = \pi r^2 \times h$

Radius (*r*)
Height (*h*)

Examples

a) Find the volume of the 3D shape below. Give your answer to 3 significant figures.

$V = a \times l$ The area of the cross-section is the area of the triangle.
$= (\frac{1}{2} \times b \times h) \times l$
$= (\frac{1}{2} \times 10 \times 7) \times 15$
$= 525\text{cm}^3$

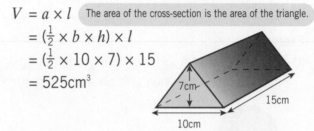

7cm
15cm
10cm

b) The diagram below shows a cylindrical oil drum. Given that 4.5 litres ≈ 1 gallon, what is the volume of oil (in gallons) that is contained in the oil drum? Use π = 3.142

❶ Work out the volume of the cylinder.
$V = \pi \times r^2 \times h$
$= 3.142 \times 28.75^2 \times 87.5$
$= 227\,242.6953\text{cm}^3$

57.5cm
87.5cm

❷ Since 1000cm³ = 1 litre, convert the volume to litres.
$\dfrac{227\,242.6953}{1000} = 227$ litres (3 s.f.)

❸ Now convert to gallons. 4.5 litres ≈ 1 gallon.
$\dfrac{227}{4.5} = 50.5$

The oil drum contains approximately 50.5 gallons of oil.

Converting volume units

Converting volume units is another tricky topic that often catches everybody out.

For example, the cube has a length of 1m, which is the same as a length of 100cm. Therefore 1m³ = 1000000cm³. Not quite what you may think! It is probably better, therefore, to change all the lengths to the same unit before starting a question.

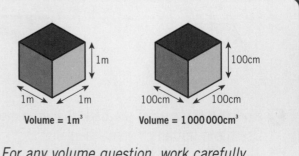

1m
1m
1m
Volume = 1m³

100cm
100cm
100cm
Volume = 1000000cm³

ⓘ *For any volume question, work carefully and show each step of your working.*

Surface area of prisms

You need to be able to find the surface area of different prisms.

Cuboid

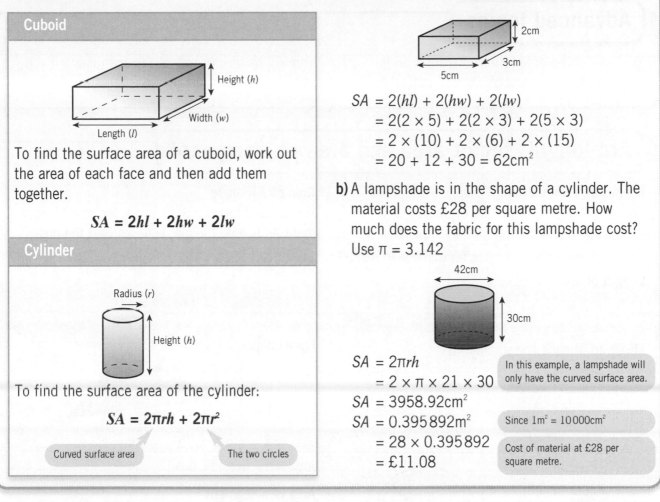

To find the surface area of a cuboid, work out the area of each face and then add them together.

$$SA = 2hl + 2hw + 2lw$$

Cylinder

To find the surface area of the cylinder:

$$SA = 2\pi rh + 2\pi r^2$$

Curved surface area   The two circles

Examples

a) Find the surface area of this cuboid.

$$SA = 2(hl) + 2(hw) + 2(lw)$$
$$= 2(2 \times 5) + 2(2 \times 3) + 2(5 \times 3)$$
$$= 2 \times (10) + 2 \times (6) + 2 \times (15)$$
$$= 20 + 12 + 30 = 62cm^2$$

b) A lampshade is in the shape of a cylinder. The material costs £28 per square metre. How much does the fabric for this lampshade cost? Use π = 3.142

$$SA = 2\pi rh$$
$$= 2 \times \pi \times 21 \times 30$$
$$SA = 3958.92cm^2$$
$$SA = 0.395892m^2$$
$$= 28 \times 0.395892$$
$$= £11.08$$

In this example, a lampshade will only have the curved surface area.

Since $1m^2 = 10\,000cm^2$

Cost of material at £28 per square metre.

Quick test

1 Work out the volumes of the following 3D shapes. Give your answers to 3 significant figures. Use π = 3.142 🔲

a)

b)

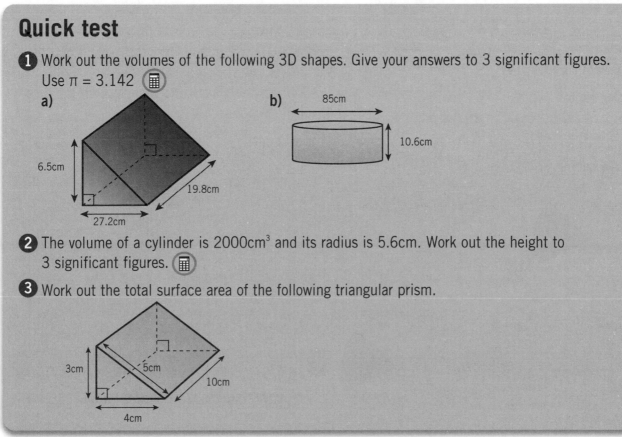

2 The volume of a cylinder is 2000cm³ and its radius is 5.6cm. Work out the height to 3 significant figures. 🔲

3 Work out the total surface area of the following triangular prism.

Further length, area & volume

Advanced topics

You need to be able to find the areas and volumes of more complex shapes and solids.

You will be given some of the formulae but you will need to learn the others.

Arc length, sector area and area of a segment

Length of a circular arc

The length of an arc can be expressed as a fraction of the circumference of the circle.

This is the angle of the sector.

Length of arc $l = \dfrac{\theta}{360°} \times 2 \times \pi \times r$

This is the circumference of the circle.

Minor arc means the smaller arc.

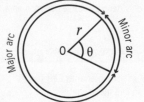

For example, length of minor arc:

$l = \dfrac{70°}{360°} \times 2 \times \pi \times 10$

$= 12.2cm$ (3 s.f.)

Area of a sector

The area of a sector can be expressed as a fraction of the area of the circle.

Area of a sector $A = \dfrac{\theta}{360°} \times \pi r^2$

This is the area of the circle.

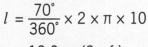

Minor sector

For example, area of minor sector:

$A = \dfrac{70°}{360°} \times \pi \times 10^2$

$= 61.1cm^2$ (3 s.f.)

Minor sector

Area of a triangle

If you know the length of two sides of a triangle and the included angle, you can find the area.

Area $= \frac{1}{2} \times a \times b \times \sin C$

Two lengths   Included angle

For example:

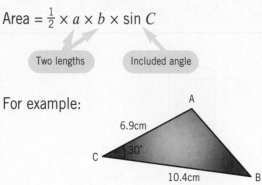

Area $= \frac{1}{2} \times 6.9 \times 10.4 \times \sin 30°$
Area $= 17.9cm^2$ (1 d.p.)

Area of a segment

The area of a **segment** can be worked out in two stages:

1. Calculate the area of the minor sector and the area of the triangle.
2. Subtract the area of the triangle from the area of the minor sector.

For example:

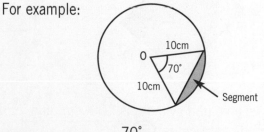

Segment

Segment area $= (\dfrac{70°}{360°} \times \pi \times 10^2) -$
$(\frac{1}{2} \times 10 \times 10 \times \sin 70°)$

$= 61.1 - 47 = 14.1cm^2$ (3 s.f.)

If you have the lengths of the radius and chord, you will need to use trigonometry in order to find the angle of the sector.

Spheres, pyramids and cones

Spheres

Volume of a sphere $= \frac{4}{3}\pi r^3$

Surface area of a sphere $= 4\pi r^2$

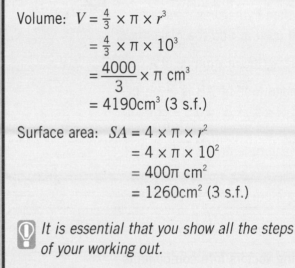

Example
Find the volume and surface area of a sphere of radius 10cm.

Volume: $V = \frac{4}{3} \times \pi \times r^3$

$= \frac{4}{3} \times \pi \times 10^3$

$= \frac{4000}{3} \times \pi$ cm³

$= 4190$cm³ (3 s.f.)

Surface area: $SA = 4 \times \pi \times r^2$

$= 4 \times \pi \times 10^2$

$= 400\pi$ cm²

$= 1260$cm² (3 s.f.)

💡 *It is essential that you show all the steps of your working out.*

Pyramids and cones
A cone is simply a pyramid with a circular base.

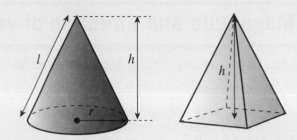

Volume of a pyramid $= \frac{1}{3} \times$ area of base $\times$ height

Volume of a cone $= \frac{1}{3} \times \pi \times r^2 \times$ height

Curved surface area of a cone $= \pi r l$ *l* is the slant height.

Example
Calculate...

a) the volume of the cone opposite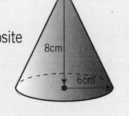

Volume $= \frac{1}{3} \times \pi \times 6^2 \times 8$

$= 96\pi$ cm³

$= 301.6$cm³

b) the total surface area of the cone.

The slant length needs to be calculated by using Pythagoras' theorem:

$l = \sqrt{8^2 + 6^2}$

$= \sqrt{100}$

$= 10$cm

Total surface area =
curved surface area + area of circle

$= \pi \times 6 \times 10 + \pi \times 6^2$

$= 60\pi + 36\pi$

Total surface area $= 96\pi = 301.6$cm²

Quick test

❶ Calculate the arc length and sector area of AOB.
Use π = 3.142 🖩

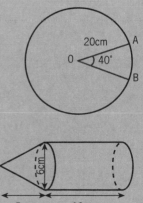

❷ Calculate the total volume of this solid, leaving your answer in terms of π.

Geometry and measures

Vectors

Magnitude and direction of vectors

Vectors have both size or magnitude and **direction**. Four types of notation are used to represent vectors.

The vector shown here can be referred to as:

$\binom{3}{2}$ or **a** or <u>a</u> or $\overrightarrow{AB}$

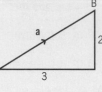

The direction of the vector is shown on the diagram by using an arrow.

If two vectors are equal then they are parallel and equal in length.

If $\overrightarrow{AB} = k\overrightarrow{CD}$, then $\overrightarrow{AB}$ and $\overrightarrow{CD}$ are parallel and the length of $\overrightarrow{AB}$ is k times the length of $\overrightarrow{CD}$.

If the vector $\mathbf{b} = \binom{4}{3}$ then the vector **-b** is in the opposite direction to **b**. $\mathbf{-b} = -1 \times \mathbf{b} = \binom{-4}{-3}$

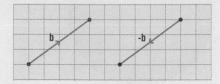

The **magnitude** of a vector is the length of the directed line segment representing it. If the vector is expressed in column form, then Pythagoras' theorem can be used to find the magnitude.

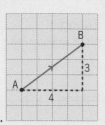

In general, the magnitude of a vector $\binom{x}{y}$ is $\sqrt{x^2 + y^2}$

The magnitude of $\overrightarrow{AB}$ is given by:
$(AB)^2 = 4^2 + 3^2 = 16 + 9 = 25$
$AB = \sqrt{25} = 5$
The magnitude of $\overrightarrow{AB}$ is 5 units.

Other important points

Adding and subtracting vectors

The **resultant** of two vectors is found by **vector addition** or **subtraction**. Vectors must always be combined end to end so that the arrows follow on from each other. A resultant is usually labelled with a double arrow.

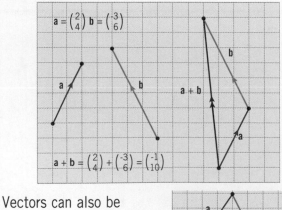

Vectors can also be subtracted. **a** – **b** can be interpreted as **a** + (**-b**).

$\mathbf{a + (-b)} = \binom{2}{3} + \binom{3}{-6} = \binom{5}{-3}$

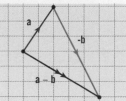

Splitting vectors into components

Any vector can be split into two components that are at 90° to each other. These two components will be $F \cos \theta$ and $F \sin \theta$.

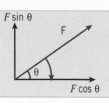

Position vectors

The position vector of a point P is the vector $\overrightarrow{OP}$ where O is the origin.

In the diagram, the position vectors of C and D are **c** and **d** respectively.

Using this notation...
- $\overrightarrow{CD} = \mathbf{-c} + \mathbf{d}$ or
  $\overrightarrow{CD} = \mathbf{d} - \mathbf{c}$

- $\overrightarrow{OM} = \mathbf{c} + \frac{1}{2}(\mathbf{d} - \mathbf{c})$
  $= \frac{1}{2}\mathbf{c} + \frac{1}{2}\mathbf{d}$
  $= \frac{1}{2}(\mathbf{d} + \mathbf{c})$

where M is the midpoint of CD.

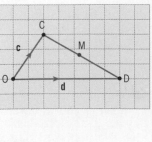

Typical GCSE questions

Examples

a)

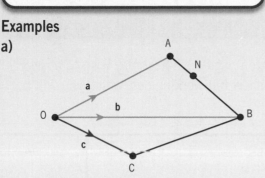

Given that $\vec{OA} = \mathbf{a}, \vec{OB} = \mathbf{b}, \vec{OC} = \mathbf{c}$ and that N splits $\vec{AB}$ in the ratio 1 : 2, find the following vectors.

i) $\vec{AC}$

$\vec{AC} = \mathbf{-a} + \mathbf{c}$ (from A to C via O)

ii) $\vec{AB}$

$\vec{AB} = \mathbf{-a} + \mathbf{b}$ (from A to B via O)

iii) $\vec{CB}$

$\vec{CB} = \mathbf{-c} + \mathbf{b}$ (from C to B via O)

iv) $\vec{AN}$

$\vec{AN} = \frac{1}{3}\vec{AB} = \frac{1}{3}(\mathbf{-a} + \mathbf{b})$

v) $\vec{ON}$

$\vec{ON} = \mathbf{a} + \frac{1}{3}(\mathbf{-a} + \mathbf{b}) = \frac{2}{3}\mathbf{a} + \frac{1}{3}\mathbf{b} = \frac{1}{3}(2\mathbf{a} + \mathbf{b})$ (via A)

Care needs to be taken when answering vector questions. Always check that the vectors you are using are end to end so that all the arrows follow on from each other and not opposite each other. Always try to simplify your answer as in Example a) part v).

b) OPQ is a triangle.

$\vec{OP} = \mathbf{a}$
$\vec{OQ} = \mathbf{b}$

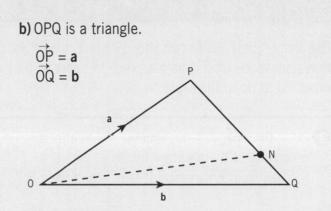

N is the point on $\vec{PQ}$ such that PN : NQ = 5 : 2. Show that $\vec{ON} = \frac{1}{7}(2\mathbf{a} + 5\mathbf{b})$

❶ Join O to N to form the triangle OPN.
$\vec{ON} - \vec{OP} + \vec{PN}$
❷ Now find $\vec{PN}$.
$\vec{PQ} = \vec{PO} + \vec{OQ}$
$\vec{PQ} = \mathbf{-a} + \mathbf{b}$
❸ $\vec{PN} = \frac{5}{7}\vec{PQ}$
Hence $\vec{PN} = \frac{5}{7}(\mathbf{-a} + \mathbf{b})$
Since $\vec{ON} = \vec{OP} + \vec{PN}$ then:
$\vec{ON} = \mathbf{a} + \frac{5}{7}(\mathbf{-a} + \mathbf{b})$
❹ Now simplify:
$\vec{ON} = \mathbf{a} - \frac{5}{7}\mathbf{a} + \frac{5}{7}\mathbf{b}$
$\vec{ON} = \frac{2}{7}\mathbf{a} + \frac{5}{7}\mathbf{b}$
$\vec{ON} = \frac{1}{7}(2\mathbf{a} + 5\mathbf{b})$

Quick test

❶ $\vec{AB} = \binom{2}{3}$, $\vec{BC} = \binom{4}{5}$, $\vec{PQ} = \binom{3}{4}$

a) Show that $\vec{AC}$ is parallel to $\vec{PQ}$.

b) Write down the ratio of the length of AC to the length of PQ.

❷ PQR is an equilateral triangle.
M is the midpoint of PR.
$\vec{PQ} = \mathbf{p}$
$\vec{QR} = \mathbf{q}$
Work out in terms of **p** and **q** expressions for the vectors...

a) $\vec{PR}$ **b)** $\vec{MQ}$.

Practice questions

Use these questions to test your progress. Check your answers on page 112. You may wish to answer these questions on a separate piece of paper so that you can show full working out, which you will be expected to do in the exam.

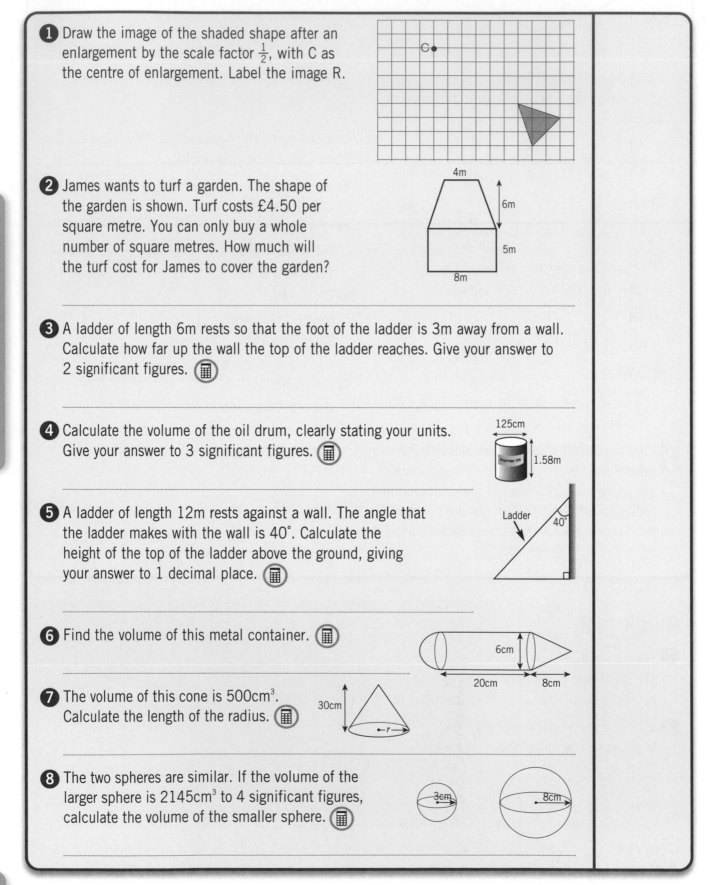

1 Draw the image of the shaded shape after an enlargement by the scale factor $\frac{1}{2}$, with C as the centre of enlargement. Label the image R.

2 James wants to turf a garden. The shape of the garden is shown. Turf costs £4.50 per square metre. You can only buy a whole number of square metres. How much will the turf cost for James to cover the garden?

4m
6m
5m
8m

3 A ladder of length 6m rests so that the foot of the ladder is 3m away from a wall. Calculate how far up the wall the top of the ladder reaches. Give your answer to 2 significant figures.

4 Calculate the volume of the oil drum, clearly stating your units. Give your answer to 3 significant figures.

125cm
1.58m

5 A ladder of length 12m rests against a wall. The angle that the ladder makes with the wall is 40°. Calculate the height of the top of the ladder above the ground, giving your answer to 1 decimal place.

Ladder
40°

6 Find the volume of this metal container.

6cm
20cm
8cm

7 The volume of this cone is 500cm³. Calculate the length of the radius.

30cm
←r→

8 The two spheres are similar. If the volume of the larger sphere is 2145cm³ to 4 significant figures, calculate the volume of the smaller sphere.

3cm
8cm

Geometry and measures

9 The diagram shows a triangle RST. B is the midpoint of RT and A is the point on RS such that AS = 2RA. $\overrightarrow{RA}$ = **r** and $\overrightarrow{RB}$ = **t**.

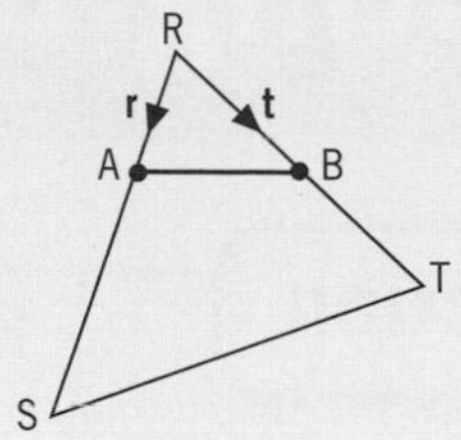

a) Write $\overrightarrow{AB}$ in terms of **r** and **t**.

_____

b) Write $\overrightarrow{AT}$ in terms of **r** and **t**.

_____

c) Write down $\overrightarrow{ST}$ in terms of **r** and **t**.

_____

10 Work out the size of the side or angle marked x in each triangle. 🖩

a)

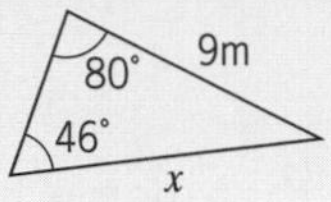

80° 9m
46°
x

b)

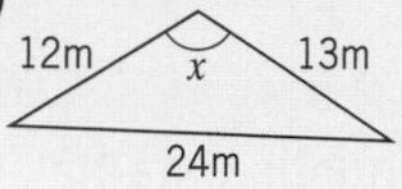

12m x 13m
24m

c)

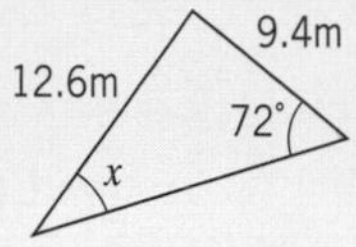

9.4m
12.6m 72°
x

d)

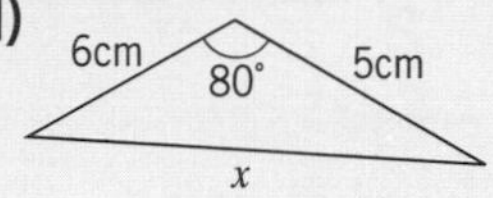

6cm 80° 5cm
x

11 In the diagram, AB represents a vertical tower on level ground. R and S are two points due west of B. The distance RS is 50m. The angles of elevation of A from S and R are 40° and 60° respectively. Calculate the height in metres of the tower, AB. 🖩

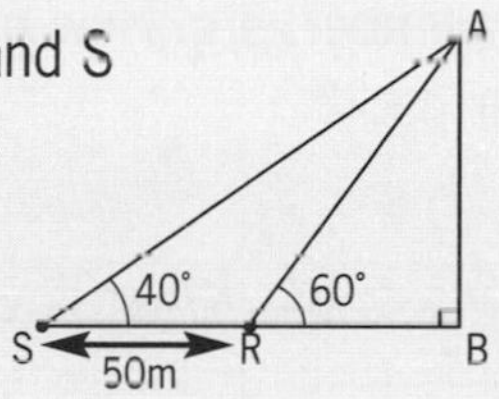

A
40° 60°
S R B
50m

12 Find the size of each of the lettered angles.

a)

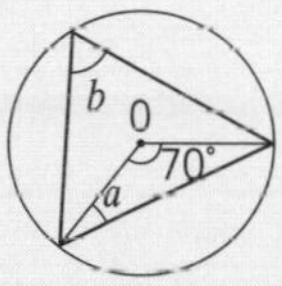

b O
70°
a

b)

a
b 122°
105°

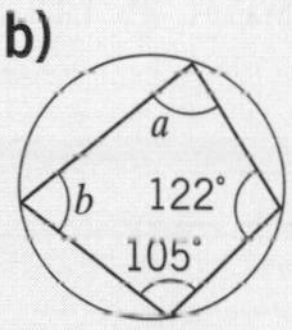

c)

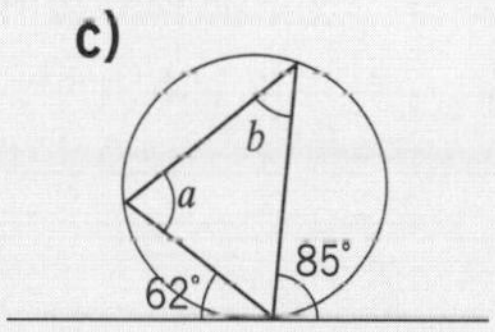

b
a
62° 85°

d)

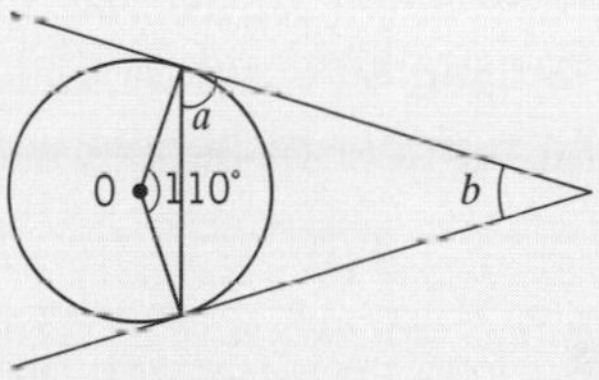

a
O 110° b

13 A garden is in the shape of a sector. Mark wants to put edging along the sides of the garden. The edging is sold in pieces 130cm long and 25cm high. He needs enough pieces to fit each side. Each piece costs £7.50. Calculate how much it will cost Mark to do the job. 🖩

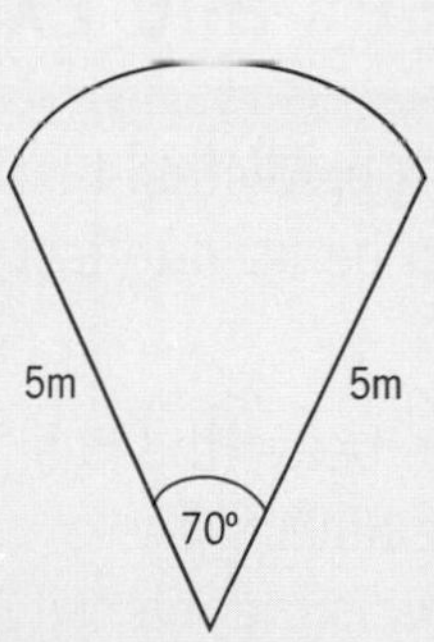

5m 5m
70°

_____

14 Calculate the length PQ of the diagonal of this cuboid, correct to 1 decimal place. 🖩

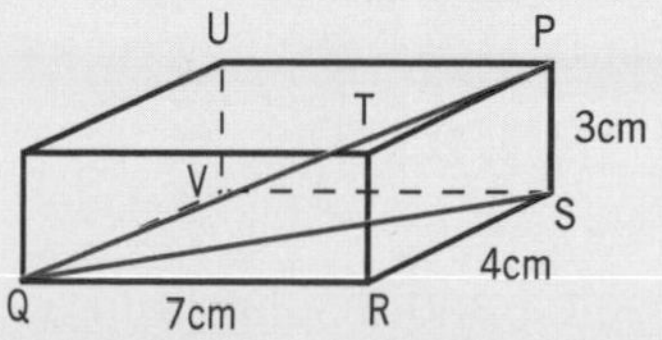

_____

_____

U P
T 3cm
V S
Q 7cm R 4cm

How well did you do?

| 0–3 | Try again | 4–7 | Getting there | 8–11 | Good work | 12–14 | Excellent! |

Collecting data

Data collection

The census is one of the largest surveys, or data collection processes, that takes place. The census is done every 10 years and its main aim is to give a 'snapshot' of Britain at the time. In order to carry out the census, all households are given a survey to complete.

Types of data

There are two main types of data:

Quantitative
The answer is a number, e.g. How many blue cars are there in a car park?

Qualitative
The answer is a word, e.g. What is your favourite colour?

Quantitative data can be discrete or continuous:
- **Discrete data** has an exact value. Each category is separate and is usually found by counting. An example is the number of people with brown hair.

- **Continuous data** has values that merge from one category to the next. Examples include the heights and weights of students. Continuous data cannot be measured exactly. The accuracy of the measurement relies on the accuracy of the measuring equipment.

Primary data is data that is collected by the person who is going to analyse and use it.
Secondary data is data that is available from an external source, such as books, newspapers and the Internet.

Hypotheses and experiments

A hypothesis is a **prediction** that can be tested. Experiments can be used to test hypotheses.

For example:
Hypothesis: The better the light, the faster seedlings grow.
Variable: This is the intensity of the light, the condition that can be changed.

Conditions: The other conditions must stay the same. All seedlings must be exactly the same size, strength and colour to start with. If there is **bias** (e.g. if one side of the tray gets more water), then the experiment needs to start again.

Two-way tables

Data can be collected and displayed in a two-way table. This is a table in which data can be read horizontally and vertically.

For example, the table shows the results of a survey of the languages studied by students in a school.

	French	Spanish	German	Total
Female	16	9	1	26
Male	12	12	8	32
Total	28	21	9	58

Questionnaires

Questionnaires can be used to test hypotheses.

When designing questionnaires...
- decide what you need to find out: the **hypothesis**
- give instructions on how the questionnaire has to be filled in
- do not ask for information that is not needed (e.g. name)
- make the questions clear and concise
- keep the questionnaire short
- if people's opinions are needed, make sure the question is **unbiased**. An example of a biased question would be: 'Do you agree that a leisure centre should have a tennis court rather than a squash court?'
- include a time period if it is needed, for example, 'For how many hours do you play computer games each week?'
- allow for all possible answers. For example, if you were asking 'Which of these is your favourite colour?', add an option for 'other'.

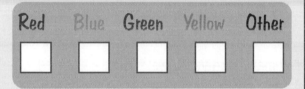

Red   Blue   Green   Yellow   Other

☐   ☐   ☐   ☐   ☐

When asked to design a questionnaire, always word the questions carefully. Try to avoid bias appearing in your questions.

Sampling

Sampling is an efficient way of collecting information about a population. It is important that the sample is representative of the population and does not contain bias. The bigger the sample, the more accurate the results will be.

Here are two methods of sampling:

Random sampling
In a random sample each member of the population has an equal chance of being chosen.

Stratified sampling
Usually the population is divided into groups (**strata**) that have something in common, such as age. A simple random sample is then taken from each group. The same proportion of the group is used for each sample.

Example
The table shows the number of girls and boys in year 11 of a school. A stratified sample of size 30 is to be taken. Calculate the number of right-handed girls to be sampled.

	Left-handed	Right-handed
Boys	14	34
Girls	12	40

14 + 12 + 34 + 40 = 100 students in total.

Fraction of population who are right-handed girls = 40

Number of right-handed girls in sample
$= \frac{40}{100} \times 30 = 12$

Quick test

1. Design a questionnaire you could give to a friend in order to find out what they do in their spare time.

2. Colin is carrying out a survey on homework; he decides to use a stratified sample and ask 100 students. Calculate the number of students he will ask from each year group.

	Frequency
Year 7	120
Year 8	150
Year 9	230

Representing data

Drawing pie charts

Pie charts illustrate data. They are circles split up into sections, each section representing a certain category of the data or number of items.

Example
The table shows the favourite sports of 24 students in year 11. Draw a pie chart to show this data.

Sport	Frequency
Football	9
Swimming	5
Netball	3
Hockey	7
Total	24

Sport	Frequency	Angle	Workings
Football	9	135°	$\frac{9}{24} \times 360°$
Swimming	5	75°	$\frac{5}{24} \times 360°$
Netball	3	45°	$\frac{3}{24} \times 360°$
Hockey	7	105°	$\frac{7}{24} \times 360°$
Total	24	360°	

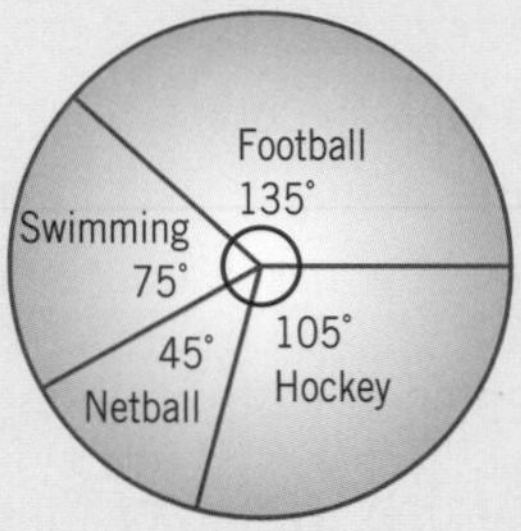

To calculate the angles for the pie chart:
❶ Find the total of the frequencies.
❷ Find the fraction of the total for each category.
❸ Multiply the fraction by 360° to find the angle.

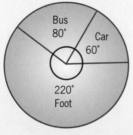

Interpreting pie charts

When the total number of items is known, the number of items in each category can be worked out.

Example
The pie chart shows how 18 students travel to school.

How many students travel by...
a) car? 360° = 18 students
$$1° = \frac{18}{360°} = 0.05$$ Work out what 1° represents.
60° × 0.05 = 3 students
b) bus? 80° × 0.05 = 4 students
c) foot? 220° × 0.05 = 11 students

Pie chart questions are usually worth about 4 marks at GCSE. Make sure the angles add up to 360° before drawing a pie chart. Measure the angles carefully since you are allowed only a 2° tolerance.

Line graphs

A line graph is a set of points joined by lines.

Year	2005	2006	2007	2008	2009	2010
Number of cars sold	2500	2900	2100	1900	1600	800

Middle values, like point A, have no meaning. Point A does **not** show that halfway between 2007 and 2008, there were 2000 cars sold. This example is known as a **times series** because the data is recorded at intervals of time.

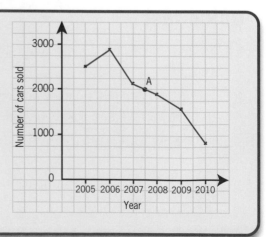

Histograms

Histograms illustrate **continuous data**. They are similar to bar charts except that there are no gaps between the bars. The data must be grouped into **equal** class intervals if the length of the bar is used to represent the frequency.

For example, the masses of 30 workers in a factory are shown in the table opposite.

$45 \leqslant W < 55$ is called a **class interval**. In this example, the class intervals are all equal in width. $45 \leqslant W < 55$ means the masses are at least 45kg but less than 55kg. A mass of 55kg would be in the next class interval.

Remember these points about histograms:
- The axes do not need to start at zero.
- The axes are labelled.
- The graph has a title.

When the class intervals are **not equal** in width, frequency is replaced with frequency density. See pages 102–103.

Mass (W kg)	Frequency
$45 \leqslant W < 55$	7
$55 \leqslant W < 65$	13
$65 \leqslant W < 75$	6
$75 \leqslant W < 85$	4

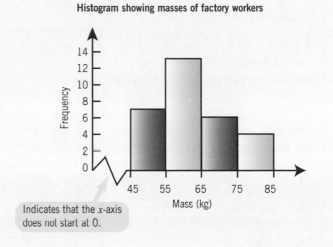

Histogram showing masses of factory workers

Indicates that the *x*-axis does not start at 0.

Frequency polygons

A frequency polygon joins the **midpoints** of the tops of the bars of **class intervals** for grouped or continuous data.

Consider the histogram of the factory workers again. To draw a frequency polygon, put a cross at the middle of the top of each bar and join up the crosses with a ruler, as shown opposite.

Make sure the frequency polygon is labelled.

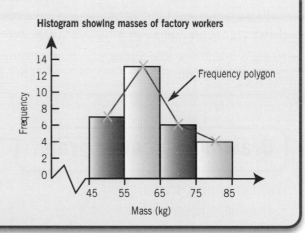

Histogram showing masses of factory workers

Frequency polygon

Quick test

1. Draw a pie chart for the set of data opposite about hair colour. 🖩

2. a) Use the histogram to complete the frequency table opposite.
   b) How many pupils were in the survey?
   c) Draw a frequency polygon on the histogram.

Hair colour	Brown	Auburn	Blonde	Black
Frequency	8	4	6	6

Height (h cm)	Frequency
$140 \leqslant h < 145$	
$145 \leqslant h < 150$	10
$150 \leqslant h < 155$	
$155 \leqslant h < 160$	
$160 \leqslant h < 165$	

Histogram showing heights of year 10 pupils

Scatter graphs & correlation

Scatter graphs

A scatter graph (scatter diagram or scatter plot) is used to show two sets of data at the same time.

Its importance is to show the correlation (connection), if any, between two sets of data.

Types of correlation

There are three types of correlation:

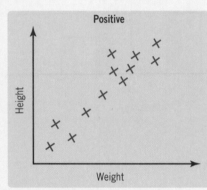

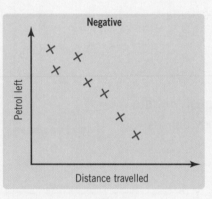

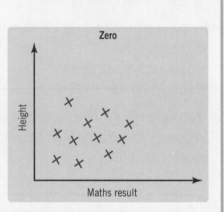

Positive correlation
Both variables are increasing. If the points are nearly in a straight line there is a strong positive correlation.

Negative correlation
One variable increases as the other decreases. If the points are nearly in a straight line there is a strong negative correlation.

Zero / no correlation
There is little or no linear relationship between the variables.

Drawing a scatter graph

When drawing a scatter graph...
- work out the scales first
- plot the points carefully
- each time a point is plotted, tick it off your list of data.

For example, the table shows the maths and history test results of 11 pupils.

Maths test (%)	76	79	38	42	49	75	83	82	66	61	54
History test (%)	70	36	84	70	74	42	29	33	50	56	64

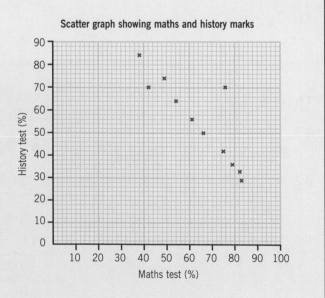

The scatter graph shows that there is a strong negative correlation – in general, the better the pupils did in maths, the worse they did in history, and vice versa.

Lines of best fit

The **line of best fit** is the line that best fits the data points on the scatter graph. It goes in the direction of the data and there is roughly the same number of points above the line as below it. A line of best fit can be used to make predictions.

For example, if Hassam was away for the maths test but got 78% in the history test, then from the scatter graph you can estimate he would have got approximately 43% in maths.

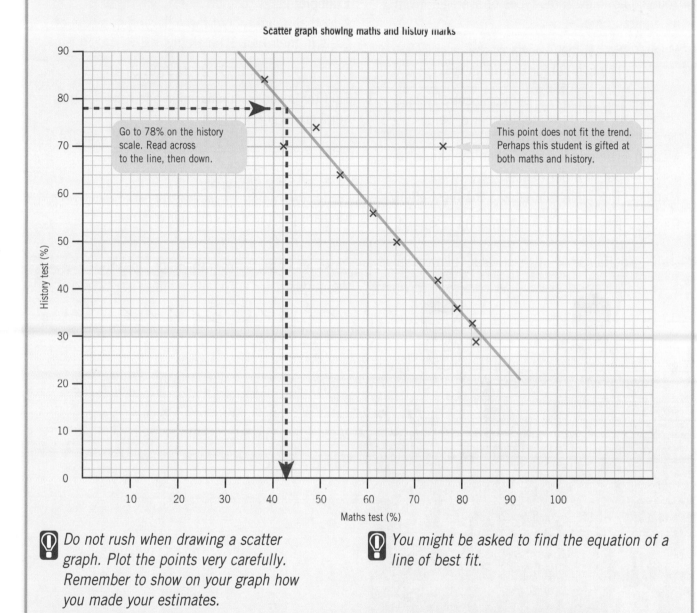

Scatter graph showing maths and history marks

Go to 78% on the history scale. Read across to the line, then down.

This point does not fit the trend. Perhaps this student is gifted at both maths and history.

History test (%)

Maths test (%)

Do not rush when drawing a scatter graph. Plot the points very carefully. Remember to show on your graph how you made your estimates.

You might be asked to find the equation of a line of best fit.

Quick test

1. Write down what type of correlation you would expect for each pair of variables.
   a) The number of pages in a magazine and the number of advertisements.
   b) The heights of students in a year group and their marks in a maths test.
   c) The height up a mountain and the temperature.
   d) The age of a used car and its value.

Averages 1

Averages of discrete data

You should know three types of average: mean, median and mode.

Mean: Sometimes known as the 'average'. The symbol for the mean is $\bar{x}$.

Mean =	$\dfrac{\text{sum of a set of values}}{\text{the number of values used}}$

Median: The **middle value** when the values are put in order of size.

Mode: The value that occurs the **most often**.

Range: How much the information is **spread**.

Range =	highest value – lowest value

Example

A football team scored the following numbers of goals in their first 10 matches.

$$2, 4, 0, 1, 2, 2, 3, 6, 2, 4$$

Find the mean, median, mode and range of the numbers of goals scored.

$$\text{Mean} = \frac{2 + 4 + 0 + 1 + 2 + 2 + 3 + 6 + 2 + 4}{10}$$

$$= \frac{26}{10} = 2.6 \text{ goals}$$

Median: put the data in order of size =
0, 1, 2, 2, 2, 2, 3, 4, 4, 6

Cross off in pairs, from the ends, to find the middle.

$$\require{cancel} \cancel{0}\ \cancel{1}\ \cancel{2}\ \cancel{2}\ (2\ \ 2)\ \cancel{3}\ \cancel{4}\ \cancel{4}\ \cancel{6}$$

$$\frac{2 + 2}{2} = 2 \text{ goals}$$

🛈 *If there are two numbers in the middle, the median is halfway between them.*

Mode = 2 goals because it occurs four times.

Range = 6 – 0 = 6

The interquartile range

The **interquartile range** is found by subtracting the **lower quartile** (LQ) from the **upper quartile** (UQ).

Interquartile range	=	upper quartile	–	lower quartile

The upper quartile is the value three quarters of the way into the distribution. The lower quartile is the value one quarter of the way into the distribution.

Finding a missing value when given the mean

If you are given the mean of a set of discrete data, you can use the information to calculate a missing value.

Example
In a modular exam, Jessica has the following results:

Module 1   72%

Module 2   49%

Module 3   63%

In order to get a grade C, Jessica needs to get an average of 67% across the four modules.

What percentage must she get in Module 4 to achieve a grade C?

Call the mark needed for Module 4, y.

$$\frac{72 + 49 + 63 + y}{4} = 67$$

$$\frac{184 + y}{4} = 67$$

$$184 + y = 67 \times 4$$

$$184 + y = 268$$

$$y = 84\%$$

Hence, Jessica needs 84% in Module 4.

Finding averages from a frequency table

A frequency table tells you how many data items there are in a group. For example:

Number of sisters (x)	0	1	2	3	4
Frequency (f)	4	9	3	5	2

This means 2 people had 4 sisters.

Mean $(\bar{x}) = \dfrac{\Sigma fx}{\Sigma f}$ (Σ means 'the sum of')

$$= \frac{(4 \times 0) + (9 \times 1) + (3 \times 2) + (5 \times 3) + (2 \times 4)}{4 + 9 + 3 + 5 + 2}$$

$$= \frac{38}{23} = 1.7 \text{ (1 d.p.)}$$

Median   Since there are 23 people who have been asked, the median will be the 12th person in the table.

11 people	12th person	11 people

The 12th person has 1 sister ∴ the median = 1

Mode   This is the data value with the highest frequency, that is 1 sister.

Range   It is the range of sisters, not the range of frequencies: 4 − 0 = 4

> *When finding the mean from a frequency table, remember to divide by the sum of the frequencies and not by how many groups there are.*

Quick test

1 Find the mean, median, mode and range of this set of data.
2, 9, 3, 6, 4, 4, 5, 8, 4

2 Charlotte made this table for the number of minutes students were late for registration.

Number of minutes late (x)	0	1	2	3	4
Frequency (f)	10	4	6	3	2

Calculate...

     a) the mean   **b)** the median   **c)** the mode   **d)** the range.

Averages 2

Stem-and-leaf diagrams

Stem-and-leaf diagrams are used for recording and displaying information. They can also be used to find the mode, median and range of a set of data.

For example, these are marks gained by some students in a mathematics exam:

24   61   55   36   42

32   60   51   38   58

55   52   47   55   55

When the information is put into a stem-and-leaf diagram it looks like this:

Stem	Leaf
2	4 ← Stem is 2, leaf is 4, value is 24.
3	6 2 8
4	2 7
5	5 1 8 5 2 5 5
6	1 0

Key: 3 | 6 = 36 marks

It is more useful to put the 'leaves' in order:

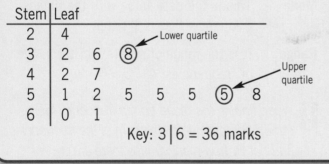

Stem	Leaf
2	4
3	2 6 ⑧ ← Lower quartile
4	2 7
5	1 2 5 5 5 ⑤ 8 ← Upper quartile
6	0 1

Key: 3 | 6 = 36 marks

To read off the values you multiply the stem by 10 and add on the leaf. Using the stem-and-leaf diagram, the mode, median, range and interquartile range can be found easily.

Mode = 55

Median = 52

Range = 61 – 24 = 37

Interquartile range = upper quartile – lower quartile

= 55 – 38 = 17

Back-to-back stem-and-leaf diagrams are particularly useful when comparing two sets of data. This back-to-back stem-and-leaf diagram shows the times, to the nearest minute, taken by some athletes to complete a cross-country run.

Men's times		Women's times
9 8 6 5	4	9
8 6 4 1 1	5	0 3 7 9
3 2 0	6	1 4 5 6 6 7 8

Key for men's times: 8 | 4 = 48 minutes
Key for women's times: 4 | 9 = 49 minutes

⓪ *Make sure you read the values the right way round.*

Using averages and spread to compare distributions

Be careful when drawing conclusions from averages as they do not always tell the whole story.

For example, the lifetime of two types of battery is tested. The mean lifetime of Trojan batteries is 9.2 hours. The mean lifetime of Warrior batteries is 11.6 hours.

From the averages, you might say that all Warrior batteries last longer than Trojan batteries. However, if you look at the range for each type of battery, you can see that this is not true:

Range of Trojan battery = 14.6 hours – 5.8 hours
= 8.8 hours

Range of Warrior battery = 13.2 hours – 9.3 hours
= 3.9 hours

Using the range, you can see that not all Warrior batteries last longer than Trojan batteries. The average lifetime of the Trojan batteries has been reduced because some of them have a particularly low lifetime.

Using appropriate averages

Choosing which average to use depends on the type of data you have and what you are looking for in it:

- The **mean** is useful when you need a 'typical' value. Be careful not to use the mean if there are extreme values.

- The **median** is a useful average if there are extreme values.
- The **mode** is useful when you need the most common value.

Averages of grouped data

When the data values are grouped into class intervals, the exact data values are not known. You can estimate the mean by using the **midpoint** of the **class interval**. The midpoint is the halfway value.

When you are using grouped (continuous) data you can only find the **modal class** as opposed to the mode. This is the class interval with the highest frequency.

> Finding the mean of grouped data is a very common GCSE question and is usually worth about 4 marks.

For example, the table below shows the masses of some year 9 students.

Mass (W kg)	Frequency (f)	Midpoint (x)	fx
$40 \leqslant W < 45$	7	42.5	297.5
$45 \leqslant W < 50$	4	47.5	190
$50 \leqslant W < 55$	3	52.5	157.5
$55 \leqslant W < 60$	1	57.5	57.5

Adding these extra columns helps to show your working out.

Mean $= \dfrac{\Sigma fx}{\Sigma f}$

$= \dfrac{(7 \times 42.5) + (4 \times 47.5) + (3 \times 52.5) + (1 \times 57.5)}{7 + 4 + 3 + 1}$

$= \dfrac{702.5}{15} = 46.8\text{kg (1 d.p.)}$

This method is the same as on page 97 except that the frequency is multiplied by the **midpoint value**.

The **modal class** is $40 \leqslant W < 45$.

Median

How to find the class interval containing the **median**:
$= \frac{1}{2}(\Sigma f + 1) = \frac{1}{2}(15 + 1) = 8$

The median is therefore the 8th year 9 student.

Mass (W kg)	Frequency	
$40 \leqslant W < 45$	7	1st to 7th student
$45 \leqslant W < 50$	4	8th to 11th student

The median lies in the class interval $45 \leqslant W < 50$.

> If your calculator will do statistical calculations, particularly Σx or Σfx, learn how to use these functions. It is much quicker but always do it twice as a check. Always try to show full working out in order to obtain some method marks.

Quick test

1 The heights of some year 10 pupils are shown in the table.

Height (h cm)	$140 \leqslant h < 145$	$145 \leqslant h < 150$	$150 \leqslant h < 155$	$155 \leqslant h < 160$	$160 \leqslant h < 165$
Frequency	4	7	14	5	2

  a) Calculate an estimate for the mean of this data. 🖩
  b) Write down the modal class.
  c) Write down the class interval that contains the median.

Cumulative frequency graphs

Cumulative frequency graphs

Cumulative frequency graphs are very useful for finding the median and the spread of grouped data.

For example, Ahmed carried out a survey for his geography coursework. He recorded the distances that 200 people travelled to an out-of-town shopping centre. The table opposite shows his findings.

You would follow these steps to create a cumulative frequency graph of Ahmed's data:

❶ To complete the cumulative frequency table add the frequencies, e.g. $12 + 49 = 61$.

❷ If the cumulative frequency table is correct, the final value in the cumulative frequency column should be the same as the number of people in the survey.

❸ Plot (5, 12), (10, 61), etc. Note that the **upper class** boundaries are used.

❹ Since no people travelled a negative distance, the graph starts at (0, 0).

❺ Join the points with a smooth curve.

Distance (d miles)	Frequency
$0 \leqslant d < 5$	12
$5 \leqslant d < 10$	49
$10 \leqslant d < 15$	57
$15 \leqslant d < 20$	45
$20 \leqslant d < 25$	34
$25 \leqslant d < 30$	3

Distance (d miles)	Cumulative frequency	
$0 \leqslant d < 5$	12	
$0 \leqslant d < 10$	61	(12 + 49)
$0 \leqslant d < 15$	118	(61 + 57)
$0 \leqslant d < 20$	163	(118 + 45)
$0 \leqslant d < 25$	197	(163 + 34)
$0 \leqslant d < 30$	200	(197 + 3)

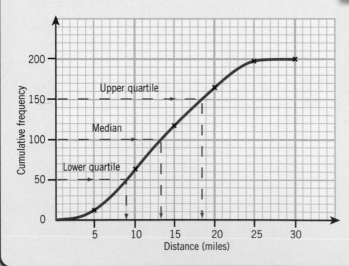

💡 *Cumulative frequency graphs are a common topic tested on the GCSE Higher level examination. Remember to...*
- *draw graphs as accurately as possible and try to avoid bumpy curves*
- *check your graph looks like an S shape*
- *plot the upper class boundaries*
- *show the method lines for the median, etc. on your graphs.*

Finding the median

The **median** is the middle value of the distribution.

For Ahmed's distance data above:
Median = $\frac{1}{2}$ × total cumulative frequency
         = $\frac{1}{2}$ × 200 = 100

Reading across from 100 to the graph and then down gives a median distance of about 13.25 miles.

Finding the interquartile range

Cumulative frequency graphs can be used to find the **interquartile range** (upper quartile – lower quartile).

Remember, the **upper quartile** is the value three quarters of the way into the distribution. So $\frac{3}{4} \times 200 = 150$, which gives an approximate value of 18.5 miles for Ahmed's data on page 100.

The **lower quartile** is the value one quarter of the way into the distribution. So $\frac{1}{4} \times 200 = 50$, which gives an approximate value of 9 miles for Ahmed's data on page 100.

The interquartile range for Ahmed's data is $18.5 - 9 = 9.5$ miles.

Using the interquartile range
A large interquartile range indicates that the 'middle half' of the data is widely spread about the median. A small interquartile range indicates that the 'middle half' of the data is concentrated about the median.

Box plots

All cumulative frequency graphs tend to have the same basic shape so it is not easy to compare two or more sets of data.

A **box plot** (or box-and-whisker diagram) shows the interquartile range as a box, which makes it useful when comparing distributions.

The box plot for the cumulative frequency graph of Ahmed's data on page 100 would look like this:

Example
The times taken (in minutes) to finish an assault course are listed in order.

8, 12, ⑫ 13, 15, ⑰ 22, 23,㉓ 27, 29
　　　 LQ　　　　Median　　　UQ

From the data find…
a) i) the lower quartile
　　　LQ = 12
　　ii) the interquartile range.
　　　UQ – LQ = 23 – 12 = 11
b) Draw a box plot for this data.

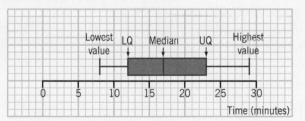

Quick test

① On another day Bethany also carried out the same survey as Ahmed. Her results are shown in the table.
　a) Draw a cumulative frequency graph of the data opposite.
　b) Work out… 🖩
　　i) the median for Bethany's data
　　ii) the interquartile range for Bethany's data.
　c) Compare Ahmed and Bethany's results.

Distance (d miles)	Frequency
$0 \leqslant d < 5$	15
$5 \leqslant d < 10$	60
$10 \leqslant d < 15$	67
$15 \leqslant d < 20$	30
$20 \leqslant d < 25$	22
$25 \leqslant d < 30$	6

Histograms

Histograms

A **histogram** is similar to a bar chart except that it is used for continuous data and the bars can be of different widths. In a histogram, the frequency is represented by the area of each bar, rather than its length or height.

Histograms with equal class intervals are covered on page 93. Here we will look at histograms with unequal class intervals.

Drawing histograms

When the bars have different widths the vertical axis is known as the **frequency density** where:

$$\text{Frequency density} = \frac{\text{frequency}}{\text{class width}}$$

Then the **areas** of the bars are proportional to the frequencies that they represent.

$$\text{Frequency} = \text{frequency density} \times \text{class width}$$

Example

The table below shows the times, in seconds, it takes people to swim 100 metres. Draw a histogram of this information.

Time (t seconds)	Frequency
$100 < t \leqslant 110$	2
$110 < t \leqslant 140$	24
$140 < t \leqslant 160$	42
$160 < t \leqslant 200$	50
$200 < t \leqslant 220$	24
$220 < t \leqslant 300$	20

To draw a histogram you need to calculate the frequency densities. Add an extra column to the table. Draw the histogram on graph paper. Make sure that there are no gaps between the bars.

Time (t seconds)	Frequency	Frequency density
$100 < t \leqslant 110$	2	$2 \div 10 = 0.2$
$110 < t \leqslant 140$	24	$24 \div 30 = 0.8$
$140 < t \leqslant 160$	42	$42 \div 20 = 2.1$
$160 < t \leqslant 200$	50	$50 \div 40 = 1.25$
$200 < t \leqslant 220$	24	$24 \div 20 = 1.2$
$220 < t \leqslant 300$	20	$20 \div 80 = 0.25$

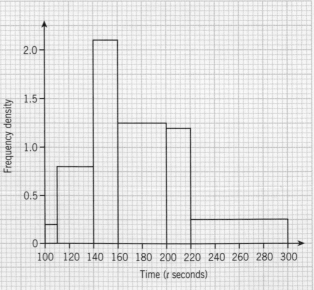

Interpreting histograms

Sometimes you may be given a histogram and asked to use the information given in it to complete the frequency table. In order to do this it is best to find the area of each bar by using:

Frequency = frequency density × class width

Example

The histogram below gives information about the ages of some runners in a marathon. Use the information in the histogram to complete the table.

Age (A years)	Frequency
$0 \leqslant A < 20$	20
$20 \leqslant A < 30$	30
$30 \leqslant A < 40$	45
$40 \leqslant A < 60$	60
$60 \leqslant A < 100$	48

The table has been completed with the figures in red.

Frequency density

Using the information in the table for this bar:
10 × 'height of bar' = 30
So the frequency density = 3
The rest of the information can then be worked out, e.g. the first bar will be 1 high, so 1 × 20 = 20, and so on.

0   20   40   60   80   100
Age (A years)

💡 *This is not a very difficult topic as long as you remember what frequency density is. This topic is a common one – you may be asked to interpret and complete a histogram all in one question.*

Quick test

1 Draw a histogram for the following information.

Number of hours (h)	Frequency
$0 \leqslant h < 20$	40
$20 \leqslant h < 30$	5
$30 \leqslant h < 60$	15
$60 \leqslant h < 70$	10
$70 \leqslant h < 100$	15

Probability 1

What is probability?

Probability is the chance or likelihood that something will happen. All probabilities lie from 0 to 1.

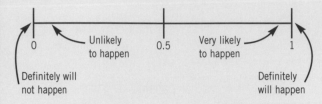

| 0 | Unlikely to happen | 0.5 | Very likely to happen | 1 |

Definitely will not happen

Definitely will happen

An event with a probability of 0.62 is more likely to happen than an event with a probability of 0.6, since 0.62 is nearer to 1.

Exhaustive events account for all possible outcomes. For example, the list HH, HT, TH, TT gives all possible outcomes when two coins are thrown simultaneously.

Mutually exclusive events are events that cannot happen at the same time. For example, if two students are chosen at random:

Event A: one student has brown hair

Event B: one student wears glasses

These are **not mutually exclusive** because brown-haired students may wear glasses.

| Probability of an event | = | number of times the event can happen / total number of possible outcomes |

P(event) is a shortened way of writing the probability of an event.

Example

There are six blue, four yellow and two red beads in a bag. John chooses a bead at random. What is the probability he chooses...

a) a red bead?

$P(\text{red}) = \frac{2}{12}$ or $\frac{1}{6}$

b) a yellow bead?

$P(\text{yellow}) = \frac{4}{12}$ or $\frac{1}{3}$

c) a blue, yellow or red bead?

$P(\text{blue, yellow or red}) = \frac{12}{12} = 1$

d) a white bead?

$P(\text{white}) = 0$

Probabilities must be written as a fraction, decimal or percentage. Probabilities can never be negative or greater than 1.

Probability of an event not happening

If two outcomes of an event are **mutually exclusive**, then:

P(outcome will happen) = 1 – P(outcome will not happen)

or

P(outcome will not happen) = 1 – P(outcome will happen)

Examples

a) The probability that someone gets flu next winter is 0.42. What is the probability that they will not get flu next winter?

P(not get flu) = 1 – P(get flu)
= 1 – 0.42
= 0.58

b) The probability that it will rain on any given day in July is $\frac{3}{11}$. What is the probability that it will not rain on a given day in July?

P(will not rain) = 1 – P(will rain)
= $1 - \frac{3}{11}$
= $\frac{8}{11}$

Relative frequencies

Relative frequencies are used to estimate probability. If it is not possible to calculate a probability, an experiment can be used to find the relative frequency.

Relative frequency of an event	=	number of times event occurred
		total number of trials

Example

When a fair dice was thrown 80 times, a six came up 12 times. What is the relative frequency of getting a six?

Number of trials = 80
Number of sixes = 12
Relative frequency = $\frac{12}{80}$ = 0.15

Expected outcome

The expected outcome of an event is also known as theoretical probability.

Examples

a) A fair dice is thrown 300 times. Approximately how many fives are likely to be obtained?

There are six possible outcomes and all are equally likely.

P(5) = $\frac{1}{6}$ × 300 = 50 fives

> Multiply 300 by $\frac{1}{6}$ since a 5 is expected $\frac{1}{6}$ of the time.

b) The probability of passing a driving test at the first attempt is 0.65. If there are 200 people taking their test for the first time, how many would you expect to fail the test?

P(fail) = 1 − 0.65
= 0.35
0.35 × 200 = 70 people are expected to fail

c) The probability that a mechanical component is faulty is 0.02. In a box containing 3000 of the mechanical components, approximately how many are likely to be faulty?

0.02 × 3000 = 60 mechanical components are likely to be faulty

Quick test

1. Write down an event that will have a probability of zero.

2. A box contains three salt and vinegar, four cheese and two bacon-flavoured packets of crisps. If a packet of crisps is chosen at random, what is the probability that it is...
   a) salt and vinegar?   b) cheese?   c) onion flavoured?

3. The probability that it will not rain tomorrow is $\frac{2}{9}$
   What is the probability that it will rain tomorrow?

4. The probability of achieving a grade C in mathematics is 0.48
   If 500 students sit the exam, how many students would you expect to achieve a grade C?

5. When a fair dice was thrown 200 times, a five came up 47 times. What was the relative frequency of getting a five?

Probability 2

The multiplication law

When two events are independent, the outcome of the second event is not affected by the outcome of the first.

If two or more events are **independent**, the probability of A and B and C... happening together is found by **multiplying** the separate probabilities.

P(A and B and C...) = P(A) × P(B) × P(C)...

Example

The probability that it will rain on any day in August is $\frac{3}{10}$. Find the probability that...

a) it will rain on both 1 August and 3 August

P(rain and rain) = $\frac{3}{10} \times \frac{3}{10} = \frac{9}{100}$

b) it will rain on 9 August but not on 20 August.

P(rain and not rain) = $\frac{3}{10} \times \frac{7}{10} = \frac{21}{100}$

The addition law

If two or more events are **mutually exclusive**, the probability of A or B or C... happening is found by **adding** the probabilities.

P(A or B or C...) = P(A) + P(B) + P(C)...

Example

There are 11 counters in a bag. Five of the counters are red and three of them are white. Lucy picks a counter at random.

Find the probability that Lucy's counter is either red or white.

P(red) = $\frac{5}{11}$

P(white) = $\frac{3}{11}$

P(red or white) = P(red) + P(white)

= $\frac{5}{11} + \frac{3}{11}$ Red and white are mutually exclusive.

= $\frac{8}{11}$

Sample space diagrams

When you are considering the possible outcomes of two events it can be helpful to draw a table. This kind of table is sometimes known as a sample space diagram.

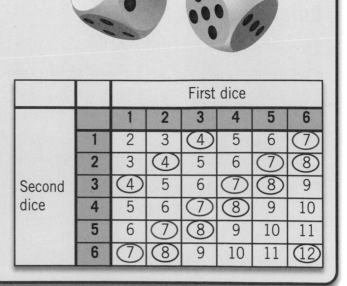

Example

Two dice are thrown together and their scores are added. Draw a diagram to show all the possible outcomes. Find the probability of...

a) a score of 7

P(score of 7) = $\frac{6}{36} = \frac{1}{6}$

b) a score that is a multiple of 4.

P(multiple of 4) = $\frac{9}{36} = \frac{1}{4}$

There are 36 possible outcomes.

		First dice					
		1	2	3	4	5	6
Second dice	1	2	3	④	5	6	⑦
	2	3	④	5	6	⑦	⑧
	3	④	5	6	⑦	⑧	9
	4	5	6	⑦	⑧	9	10
	5	6	⑦	⑧	9	10	11
	6	⑦	⑧	9	10	11	⑫

Tree diagrams

Tree diagrams are another way of showing the possible outcomes of two or more events. They may be written horizontally or vertically.

Example

Thomas has 11 sweets in a bag. Five of the sweets are orange and the rest are red. Thomas takes at random two sweets from the bag. Work out the probability that the sweets will be one of either colour.

① Draw a tree diagram for this information:

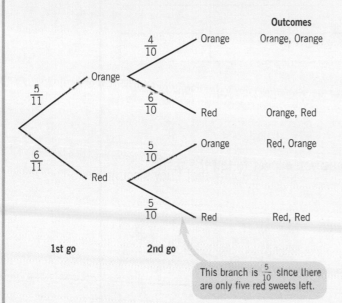

This branch is $\frac{5}{10}$ since there are only five red sweets left.

② Put the probabilities on the branches. Since the first sweet is not replaced after the first go, there are now only 10 sweets left in the bag.

③ The multiplication and addition laws are useful when answering questions about tree diagrams. To find the probability that the sweets will be one of either colour:

P(orange and red) or P(red and orange)

$$= \left(\frac{5}{11} \times \frac{6}{10}\right) + \left(\frac{6}{11} \times \frac{5}{10}\right)$$

$$= \frac{30}{110} + \frac{30}{110}$$

$$= \frac{60}{110}$$

$$= \frac{6}{11}$$

Remember...
- P(A and B) = P(A) × P(B)
- P(A or B) = P(A) + P(B)

When answering questions that involve tree diagrams, remember to...
- *make sure that on each pair of branches the probabilities add up to 1*
- *multiply along the branches*
- *add the probabilities when there is more than one alternative route, i.e. P(A or B).*

Quick test

① The probability that Meena does her homework is 0.8
   The probability that Fiona does her homework is 0.45
   Find the probability that both girls do their homework.

② a) Draw a sample space diagram that shows the possible outcomes when two dice are thrown together and their scores are multiplied.
   b) What is the probability of a score of 6?
   c) What is the probability of a score of 37?

③ A bag contains three red and four blue counters. If a counter is taken out of the bag at random, its colour noted and then it is replaced, and a second counter is taken out, what is the probability of choosing one counter of each colour? (Use a tree diagram to help you.)

Practice questions

Use these questions to test your progress. Check your answers on page 112. You may wish to answer these questions on a separate piece of paper so that you can show full working out, which you will be expected to do in the exam.

Statistics and probability

1 A youth club has 75 members, of which 42 are boys.
There are 15 members who are boys under 13 years old.
There are 21 members who are girls aged 13 and over.

	Under 13 years old	13 years old and over	Totals
Boys			
Girls			
Total			

a) Complete the two-way table.

b) How many of the girls are under 13 years old?

2 The probability of passing a driving test is 0.7
If 200 people take the test today, how many would you expect to fail the test?

3 The masses of some students in a class are measured. The results are shown in the table.

a) Work out an estimate for the mean mass of the students. 🖩

b) What is the modal class?

Mass (M kg)	Number of students
$40 \leqslant M < 45$	6
$45 \leqslant M < 50$	5
$50 \leqslant M < 55$	8
$55 \leqslant M < 60$	4
$60 \leqslant M < 65$	2

4 Amir and Matthew are going to take a swimming test. The probability that Amir will pass the swimming test is 0.85. The probability that Matthew will pass the swimming test is 0.6. The two events are independent.

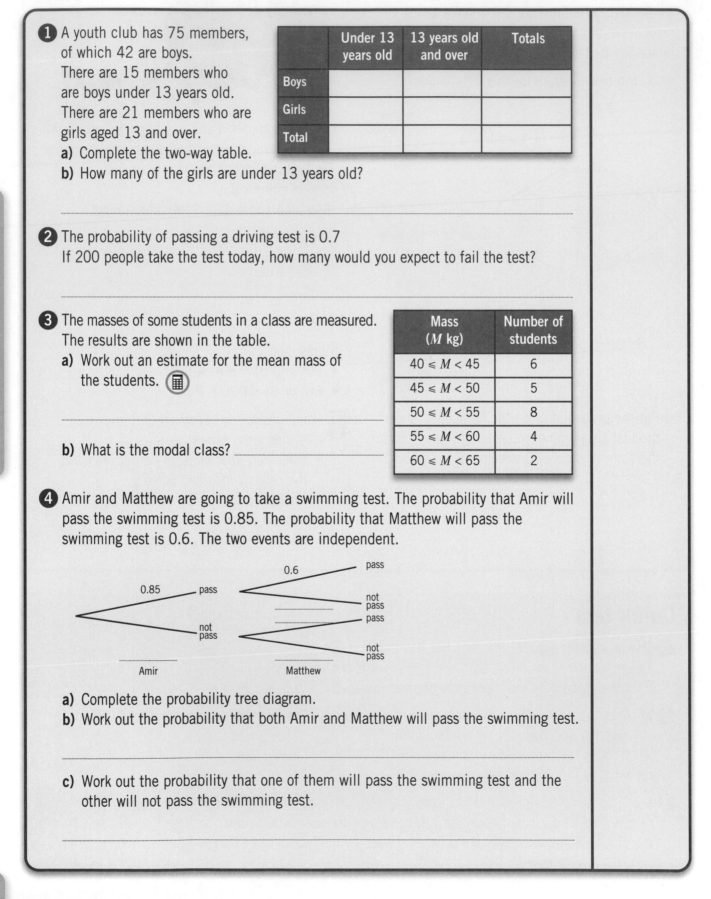

a) Complete the probability tree diagram.

b) Work out the probability that both Amir and Matthew will pass the swimming test.

c) Work out the probability that one of them will pass the swimming test and the other will not pass the swimming test.

5 The table shows the times, in minutes, for 83 people's journeys to work.

a) Complete the cumulative frequency column in the table.

b) Draw a cumulative frequency graph of the data.

c) From your graph find the median.

....

d) From your graph find the interquartile range.

....

e) How many people had a journey of more than 45 minutes to work?

Time (t minutes)	Frequency	Cumulative frequency
$0 \leqslant t < 10$	5	
$10 \leqslant t < 20$	20	
$20 \leqslant t < 30$	26	
$30 \leqslant t < 40$	18	
$40 \leqslant t < 50$	10	
$50 \leqslant t < 60$	4	

6 The table shows the working life of 60 batteries. Draw a histogram of this information.

Number of hours (h)	Frequency
$0 \leqslant h < 5$	9
$5 \leqslant h < 20$	15
$20 \leqslant h < 30$	18
$30 \leqslant h < 50$	10
$50 \leqslant h < 60$	8

7 A bag contains four red and three green beads. A bead is taken from the bag at random. A second bead is then taken. What is the probability that...

a) both beads are red? ....

b) the beads are different colours? ....

8 Lucy is doing a survey into whether people play sport. She decides to ask 50 people by standing outside a sports centre on a Wednesday morning. Explain why her survey will be biased.

....

9 The box plots show the ages of males and females at a sports centre. Compare and contrast the two box plots.

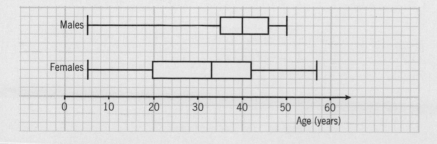

How well did you do?

| 0–2 | Try again | 3–5 | Getting there | 6–7 | Good work | 8–9 | Excellent! |

Answers

Number   Quick test answers

Page 5   Using a calculator
1. a) 14.45   b) 769.6   c) 7.052   d) $8\frac{1}{3}$ or 8.3̇

Page 7   Types of numbers
1. 11, 13, 17, 19, 23, 29   **2.** HCF: 12; LCM: 120   **3.** a) ±8 b) 6
4. a) $\frac{12}{9}$ b) $\frac{p}{x}$ c) $\frac{1}{5}$ d) 10

Page 9   Positive & negative numbers
1. 3°C
2. a) 4   b) -16   c) -12   d) -12   e) 5   f) 6   g) 7   h) -10   i) 36

Page 11   Fractions
1. a) $\frac{1}{3}$ b) $\frac{7}{20}$ c) $\frac{6}{13}$ d) $1\frac{1}{3}$ e) $\frac{5}{21}$ f) $\frac{4}{21}$ g) $\frac{49}{121}$ h) $\frac{50}{63}$
2. £40   **3.** 247mm

Page 13   Decimals
1. a) 36.48   b) 17.679   c) 26.88   d) 12.3   e) 6   f) 52   g) 0.4
   h) 0.0037   i) 4000   j) 45 000   k) 470 000   l) 32 500
2. a) 7.47   b) 12.04   c) 9.37   d) 10.04   e) 8.18

Page 15   Approximations & checking calculations
1. a) 0.00379   b) 27 500   c) 307 000
2. 100   **3.** 10 rolls   **4.** £7.45 (check: 175 ÷ 25 = 7✓)   **5.** 6700km

Page 17   Percentages 1
1. £210   **2.** 74.6%   **3.** 9.9lb   **4.** £411.76   **5.** Super's; £33.33

Page 19   Percentages 2
1. £161.50   **2.** a) £1800   b) £6180   **3.** £199 500   **4.** £3496.73

Page 20   Fractions, decimals & percentages
1. a) i) 0.2857   ii) 0.6̇   iii) 0.8̇   b) i) 28.57%   ii) 60%   iii) 88.8̇%
2. 0.041, 5%, 26%, $\frac{1}{3}$, $\frac{2}{5}$, 0.42

Page 21   Recurring decimals & surds
1. a) $\frac{15}{99} = \frac{5}{33}$ b) $\frac{7}{9}$ c) $\frac{281}{990}$
2. a) $5\sqrt{3}$ b) $10\sqrt{5}$ c) $11 - 6\sqrt{2}$ d) $4\sqrt{2} - \sqrt{6} + 18$ e) $\frac{\sqrt{3}}{3}$

Page 23   Ratio
1. a) 4 : 5   b) 1 : 2   c) 5 : 2
2. 10, 15 and 35 sweets respectively   **3.** £2.76   **4.** 36cm

Page 25   Indices
1. a) 12^{12} b) 9^{-6} c) 18^8 d) 4^{10}
2. a) x^{13} b) $6x^{13}$ c) $4x^2$ d) $5x^{11}$ e) $2x^{12}$
3. a) 1   b) 1   c) 16   d) $\frac{1}{125}$ e) 12   f) $\frac{1}{6}$ 4. a) $\frac{1}{16x^2}$ b) $\frac{1}{36x^4y^8}$

Page 27   Standard index form
1. a) 6.3×10^5 b) 2.73×10^3 c) 4.29×10^5 d) 6.3×10^{-7}
2. a) 6×10^{12} b) 1.22×10^9 c) 4×10^3 d) 3×10^{18}
3. a) 4.35×10^{10} b) 4.59×10^{16}
4. 9.76×10^{10}

Page 29   Upper & lower bounds of measurement
1. Upper bound = 0.65; Lower bound = 0.64
2. Upper bound = 56.375; Lower bound = 51.675

Pages 30–31   Answers to practice questions
1. £25 000
2. a) 365   b) 0.706
3. $\frac{9 + 9}{0.2 \times 50} = \frac{18}{10} = 1.8$
4. a) $60 = 2 \times 2 \times 3 \times 5 = 2^2 \times 3 \times 5$ b) 300
5. The 100ml of toothpaste, since 50ml costs 2.48p per ml, 75ml costs 2.61p per ml and 100ml costs 2.42p per ml.
6. £376.47
7. £6502.50
8. £445.97

9. 20%
10. a) 2.67×10^6 b) 4.27×10^3 c) 3.296×10^{-2} d) 2.7×10^{-2}
11. a) 1.2×10^{22} b) 2×10^{11}
12. a) $\frac{4}{9}$ b) $\frac{21}{99} = \frac{7}{33}$ c) $\frac{234}{999} = \frac{26}{111}$ d) $\frac{25}{90} = \frac{5}{18}$
13. a) $2\sqrt{3}$ b) $5\sqrt{6}$ c) $10\sqrt{2}$ d) $3\sqrt{2} - 2\sqrt{6}$ e) 15
14. £313.19
15. 1 562 500 bacteria
16. Upper bound = 13.28m/s (2 d.p.); Lower bound = 13.04m/s (2 d.p.)
17. Upper bound = 6.7349cm (4 d.p.); Lower bound = 6.7112cm (4 d.p.)
18. a) 4   b) 4   c) $\frac{1}{36}$ d) 7   e) $\frac{1}{5}$ f) $\frac{1}{16}$ g) $\frac{49}{25}$
19. Sarah is not correct. $\sqrt{2}$ is irrational since a rational number can be written as a fraction and $\sqrt{2}$ cannot.
20. a) Irrational   b) Rational   c) Irrational   d) Irrational   e) Rational

Algebra   Quick test answers

Page 33   Algebra 1
1. a) $10a$ b) $8a + b$ c) $9x + 4y$ d) $4x^2y - 5xy^2$
2. a) 12   b) 128   c) 6
3. a) $3x + 6$ b) $2x + 2y$ c) $-6x - 12$ d) $x^2 + 8x + 15$ e) $y^2 - 7y + 12$
   f) $a^2 + 4a + 4$
4. -15

Page 35   Algebra 2
1. a) $3(x + 3)$ b) $5(y - 3)$ c) $6x(2x - 1)$ d) $(x + 1)(x - 6)$
   e) $(x - 1)(x - 2)$ f) $(x - 4)(x + 4)$ g) $(2x - 1)(x - 3)$
   h) $(3x + 1)(2x + 1)$
2. a) $\frac{5x + 4}{(x + 2)(x - 1)}$
   b) $\frac{(s + 2)(s - 1)}{6(s + 3)}$
   c) $\frac{18(a + b)(a + 1)}{(a + 2)}$

Page 37   Equations 1
1. a) $x = 6$ b) $x = 4.5$ c) $x = 2$ d) $x = 4$ e) $x = -1$ f) $x = -1.4$
   g) $x = 1, x = -5$ h) $x = 2, x = 3$ i) $x = \frac{1}{3}, x = 2$ j) $x = -\frac{1}{2}, x = -2$

Page 39   Equations 2
1. a) $x = -4.5, y = 4$ b) $a = 2, b = 1$
2. $x = 3, y = -1$
3. 3.3

Page 40   Number patterns & sequences
1. a) 13, 15   b) 25, 36   c) 4, 2
2. a) $2n + 3$ b) $3n - 1$ c) $4n + 2$ d) $10 - 2n$

Page 41   Inequalities
1. a) $x < 6$ b) $x \geqslant 4$ c) $1 \leqslant x \leqslant 3$ d) $\frac{-1}{5} \leqslant x < 2$

Page 43   Formulae
1. a) -16.84   b) 118.52   c) 8.173̇   d) 475.24
2. $u = \pm\sqrt{v^2 - 2as}$
3. $R = \frac{V}{I}$
4. $r = \frac{-(y + ps)}{(p - 1)}$ or $\frac{(y + ps)}{(1 - p)}$

Page 44   The quadratic formula
1. a) $x = -0.35$ or $x = -5.65$ b) $x = 4.21$ or $x = -0.71$
   c) $x = 2.46$ or $x = -1.46$

Page 45   Direct & inverse proportion
1. $y = 1$ (equation: $y = \frac{100}{x^2}$)
2. $p = 21$ (equation: $p = 3\sqrt{t}$)
3. $r = 1.587$ (equation: $s = \frac{40}{r^3}$)

Page 47   Straight-line graphs
1. a) $x = 1$ b) $x = 1.5$

2. a) Gradient 2, intercept (0, 4) **b)** Gradient 3, intercept (0, -2)
   c) Gradient 3, intercept (0, 2)

Page 49   Curved graphs

1. a)

x	-3	-2	-1	0	1	2	3
y	-24	-5	2	3	4	11	30

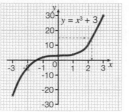

   b) The coordinates that need to be plotted are:
   (3, 30), (2, 11), (1, 4), (0, 3), (-1, 2), (-2, -5), (-3, -24)
   c) When $y = 15$, $x = 2.3$ (to 1 d.p.)
2. Graph A: $y = 3 - x^2$ Graph B: $y = \frac{2}{x}$ Graph C: $y = 5 - x$ Graph D: $y = x^3$

Page 51   Advanced graphs

1. a) 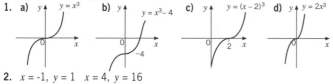 $y = x^3$ **b)** $y = x^3 - 4$ **c)** $y = (x - 2)^3$ **d)** $y = 2x^3$

2. $x = -1$, $y = 1$ $x = 4$, $y = 16$

Page 53   Interpreting graphs

1. Container A, graph C; Container B, graph A; Container C, graph B
2. a) $x = -2.8, 1.8$ **b)** $x = -1.4, 1.4$ **c)** $x = 2.7, -0.7$

Pages 54–55   Answers to practice questions

1. a) $x = 3$ **b)** $x = 4$ **c)** $x = 5$ **d)** $x = 2$ **e)** $x = 1$
2. a) $5n + 2$ **b)** $3n^2 + 2$
3. a) $12x^4$ **b)** $12x^5y^3$ **c)** $4y^3$ **d)** $9y^4$
4. $a = 3$, $b = -2$
5. a) $p = 54.3$ (3 s.f.) **b)** $y = \frac{p^2 + 3r^2}{5x}$
6. $x = 1.8$
7. $1 \leq n \leq 3$
8. a) $y = x^2 - 4$ is graph D **b)** $y = 2x + 1$ is graph B
   c) $y = 3 - 4x$ is graph A **d)** $xy = 6$ is graph C
9. a) $\frac{5x + 8}{(x + 4)(x - 2)}$ **b)** $\frac{4x + 30}{(x - 3)(x + 4)}$ **c)** $\frac{1}{2}$

10. $\frac{x^2 - 16}{2x^2 - 11x + 12} = \frac{(x - 4)(x + 4)}{(2x - 3)(x - 4)} = \frac{x + 4}{2x - 3}$

11. a) $x = 1.72$, $x = -0.387$ **b)** $x = 0.839$, $x = -0.239$
12. a) $(2x + 4)(x - 1) = 50$
       $2x^2 + 2x - 4 = 50$
       $2x^2 + 2x - 54 = 0$
       $x^2 + x - 27 = 0$
   b) $x = 4.72$, length $= 13.44$cm
13. $x = 0$ $y = 4$
   $x = -4$ $y = 0$
   The line $y = x + 4$ intersects the circle $x^2 + y^2 = 16$ at (0, 4) and (-4, 0)
14. $p = \frac{4x - 2r}{6 + x}$
15. a) Move graph 2 units to left, a translation of $\binom{-2}{0}$.
   b) Move graph 3 units down the y-axis, a translation of $\binom{0}{-3}$.
   c) Reflect the graph in the x-axis.
   d) Multiply all x values by $\frac{1}{2}$, i.e. a stretch of scale factor $\frac{1}{2}$ parallel
       to the x-axis.
16. a) Amy = $2y$ and Beth = $2y + 1$
       Hence Cara has: $\frac{2y}{3} + \frac{2y + 1}{5} = 5$
   b) $\frac{10y + 3(2y + 1)}{15} = 5$
       $10y + 6y + 3 = 5 \times 15$
       $16y + 3 = 75$
       $16y = 72$, so $y = £4.50$
       Beth keeps $\frac{4}{5}(2y + 1) = \frac{4}{5} \times 10 = £8$

Geometry and measures   **Quick test answers**

Page 57   Constructions & plans

1. 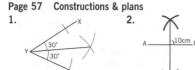   **2.**

Page 59   Angles

1. a) $a = 150°$ **b)** $b = 70°$, $c = 110°$, $d = 70°$
   c) $a = 50°$, $b = 50°$, $c = 130°$, $d = 50°$

2. a) 60° **b)** 120°

Page 61   Bearings & scale drawings

1. a) 072° **b)** 305° **c)** 145°
2. a) 252° **b)** 125° **c)** 325°
3. 7km

Page 63   Transformations 1

1. a)–d)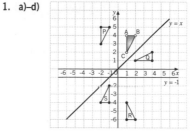

2. Move 2 to the left and 3 upwards.
3. $\binom{-5}{11}$

Page 65   Transformations 2

1.    **2. a)–b)**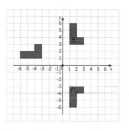

Page 67   Similarity & congruency

1. a) 11.6cm **b)** 14cm
2. 15.9cm
3. Yes, because SAS, i.e. two sides and included angle are equal.
4. 90cm²

Page 68   Loci & coordinates in 3D

1.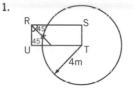

Page 69   Angle properties of circles

1. $a = 84°$, $b = 20°$, $c = 94°$, $d = 86°$

Page 71   Pythagoras' theorem

1. a) 17.2cm **b)** 20.0cm **2.** 17cm **3.** 94.3km

Page 73   Trigonometry in right-angled triangles

1. a) **b)** **c)**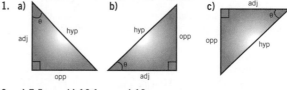

2. a) 7.5cm **b)** 10.1cm **c)** 18cm
3. a) 25.6° **b)** 62.3° **c)** 36.9°

Page 75   Application of trigonometry

1. 35.8m **2. a)** 20cm **b)** 68.0cm **c)** 17.1° **3. a)** 25cm **b)** 11.3°

Page 77   Further trigonometry

1. a) 8.08cm **b)** 28.4° **c)** 28.0° **d)** 68.83m
2. 41.8°, 138.2°

Page 79   Measures & measurement

1. 3.5kg **2.** 6.6lb **3.** $10\frac{1}{2}$ pints **4.** $9.15 \leq 9.2 < 9.25$
5. $57.5 \leq 58 < 58.5$ **6.** 2.25mph
7. 8.57 hours (or 8 hours 34 minutes) **8.** 2.2g/cm³

Page 81   Area of 2D shapes

1. a) 64cm² **b)** 60cm² **c)** 63.6cm² **d)** 208cm² **2.** 21.5cm²

Page 83   Volume of 3D shapes

1. a) 1750cm³ **b)** 60 200cm³ **2.** 20.3cm **3.** 132cm²

Answers

Page 85 Further length, area & volume
1. Arc length = 13.96cm; sector area = 139.6cm² 2. 105πcm³

Page 87 Vectors
1. a) Since $\vec{AC} = \begin{pmatrix} 6 \\ 8 \end{pmatrix}$ and $\vec{PQ} = \begin{pmatrix} 3 \\ 4 \end{pmatrix}$ then $2\vec{PQ} = \vec{AC}$ so they are parallel.
   b) Ratio 2 : 1
2. a) $\vec{PR}$ = p + q b) $\vec{MQ} = \frac{1}{2}$(p – q)

Pages 88–89 Answers to practice questions
1.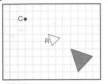
2. £342
3. 5.2m
4. 1.94m³
5. 9.2m
6. 697.43cm³
7. 3.99cm (2 d.p.)
8. 113.1cm³
9. a) -r + t b) -r + 2t c) -3r + 2t
10. a) 12.32m b) 147.5° c) 45.2° d) 7.11cm
11. 81.4m
12. a) a = 55°; b = 35° b) a = 75°; b = 58° c) a = 85°; b = 62°
    d) a = 55°; b = 70°
13. £97.50
14. 8.6cm

Statistics and probability Quick test answers

Page 91 Collecting data
1. Your questionnaire should follow the guidance given on page 91.
2. Year 7 – 24; Year 8 – 30; Year 9 – 46

Page 93 Representing data
1. The angles for the pie chart are: Brown 120°, Auburn 60°, Blonde 90°, Black 90°
2. a) The frequencies for the heights are: $140 \leqslant h < 145$ = 6, $145 \leqslant h < 150$ = 10, $150 \leqslant h < 155$ = 11, $155 \leqslant h < 160$ = 5, $160 \leqslant h < 165$ = 2
   b) 34 pupils
   c) The frequency polygon should be plotted at the midpoints of the bars.

Page 95 Scatter graphs & correlation
1. a) Positive b) Zero or no correlation c) Negative d) Negative

Page 97 Averages 1
1. Mean = 5; median = 4; mode = 4; range = 7
2. a) 1 min 19 secs b) 1 min c) 0 mins d) 4 mins

Page 99 Averages 2
1. a) 151.56 b) $150 \leqslant h < 155$ c) $150 \leqslant h < 155$

Page 101 Cumulative frequency graphs
1. a) A cumulative frequency graph with the following points should be plotted: (5, 15), (10, 75), (15, 142), (20, 172), (25, 194), (30, 200).
   b) i) 11.5 miles (approx.) ii) 8 miles (approx.)
   c) The median distance travelled is less when Bethany did her survey, and the interquartile range is also slightly smaller than when Ahmed did his survey.

Page 103 Histograms
1.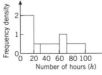

Page 105 Probability 1
1. **Any sensible answer, e.g.:** I will get a 7 when I throw a dice; I will get a 4 when I toss a coin.
2. a) $\frac{1}{3}$ b) $\frac{4}{9}$ c) 0 3. $\frac{7}{9}$ 4. 240 5. $\frac{47}{200}$ = 0.235

Page 107 Probability 2
1. 0.36
2. a)

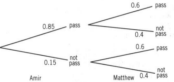

		Dice 1				
		1	2	3	4	5	6
Dice 2	1	1	2	3	4	5	6
	2	2	4	6	8	10	12
	3	3	6	9	12	15	18
	4	4	8	12	16	20	24
	5	5	10	15	20	25	30
	6	6	12	18	24	30	36

   b) $\frac{4}{36} = \frac{1}{9}$ c) 0 3. $\frac{24}{49}$

Pages 108–109 Answers to practice questions
1. a)

	Under 13 years old	13 years old and over	Total
Boys	15	27	42
Girls	12	21	33
Total	27	48	75

   b) 12
2. 60 people
3. a) 50.7kg b) $50 \leqslant M < 55$
4. a)

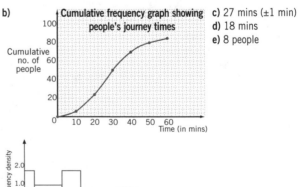

   b) 0.51
   c) 0.43
5. a)

Time (t mins)	Frequency	Cumulative frequency
$0 \leqslant t < 10$	5	5
$10 \leqslant t < 20$	20	25
$20 \leqslant t < 30$	26	51
$30 \leqslant t < 40$	18	69
$40 \leqslant t < 50$	10	79
$50 \leqslant t < 60$	4	83

   b)

c) 27 mins (±1 min)
d) 18 mins
e) 8 people

6.

7. a) $\frac{12}{42} = \frac{2}{7}$ b) $\frac{24}{42} = \frac{4}{7}$
8. **A good answer would include the following points:** Lucy will not be able to ask those people who work on a Wednesday morning; people who go to a sports centre generally play sport.
9. **A good answer would include the following points:** the median age of the males is 40 whereas for females it is 33, hence the males' median age is greater; the interquartile range for females is much greater than for the males, hence there is a much greater spread of female ages compared to male ages; more older females than older males go to the sports centre.